THE TWIN THIEVES

HOW GREAT LEADERS BUILD GREAT TEAMS

STEVE JONES & LUCAS JADIN

THE FEAR OF FAILURE

THE FEAR OF JUDGEMENT

THE TWIN THIEVES

THE TWIN THIEVES

How Great Leaders Build Great Teams

By Steve Jones and Lucas Jadin

FOREWORD

I WILL NEVER FORGET WHEN I told Lucas he was going to join my brand. I was sitting at Fire and Ice in Lake Tahoe on my birthday, and after I hung up, I told my girlfriend, this kid is special.

For years I've been telling people that reach out wanting to work with me that Lucas is who they really want. His ability to understand team and interpersonal dynamics is unlike anyone I've ever known. His passion for the science is unmatched, and it has shown up in his results and why clients absolutely love him.

I begged him to stop teaching high school and focus on writing, speaking, and workshops, but he didn't listen. Those high school kids are really important to him. Now, watching how he has a client roster of world champions, professional athletes, college coaches, and CEO's, it amazing to me that high school kids get to have someone like that still working with them!

When Lucas told me he was going to write this book with Steve, I was thrilled for him and you. Because the amount of wisdom the two of them have individually is rare to find in a single person, and together, well it's unheard of.

Steve's track record in high school football is the stuff of legends, with only three games lost in the last 100 he has coached. His culture of love, and his belief that people are not production units has generated so much buzz that he is a highly sought after speaker and consultant for many industries.

The practical wisdom you will find in this easy-to-read fable is the stuff I would have given anything to have had the coaches I played for to have had access to. If you didn't know what these guys brought to the table, you will be in for a treat. And if you already know them, then you know you are in for one of those books you will read over and over again that will be covered in notes, highlights and ideas.

Love,
Joshua Medcalf

CONTENTS

CHAPTER 1

HEARTBREAK

"COACH! WE NEED a call!"

Under the brim of his red visor, Coach Mike Frost was expressionless. His heart pounded. His mind raced. It was only the first round of the state playoffs, and the coach knew his team couldn't afford yet another early playoff exit.

He glanced up at the scoreboard. Westlake Aviators 27, Columbus Warriors 28.

Coach Frost took off his headset and looked at the players. Some looked nervously at the ground. Others stared at him, paralyzed, searching for direction. He could feel the fear radiating off their exhausted bodies.

The Aviators had jumped out to a 21–0 lead early in the game, but the wheels came off after halftime. They looked like a completely different team, and the Warriors stormed back to take the lead in the middle of the fourth quarter.

Fortunately, the Aviators scored their lone touchdown of the second half as the clock expired, leaving Coach Frost with two choices: send out the kick team for the easy extra point, or go for two and end it right here.

Coach Frost used his last timeout to think it over. His offensive coordinator's voice piped into his headset.

"Coach, I say we go for the jugular. We haven't moved the ball since the second quarter. Let's go for two and end this thing right now."

Coach Frost mulled the suggestion over. His stomach sank. Fear crept in.

"Give me a sec. I wanna think about it," Coach Frost said.

Despite the thousands of loyal fans decked out in Aviator gear cheering them on, the huddle of players and coaches felt like a lonely place. Nobody said it, but everybody was thinking the same thing.

We can't blow this again...
Everybody is counting on us...
We'll always be the ones that couldn't finish in the playoffs...

The Aviators were at their best when playing aggressively, but it was clear that right now they were just out there trying not to lose.

An assistant piped into Coach Frost's headset, breaking his concentration.

"We don't have much time, Coach. We need the call."

Coach Frost wanted nothing more than to get out of this playoff slump and for his players to experience the feeling of a big playoff win.

"All right, guys. Let's finish this game off in overtime! Kicking team! On the field!"

As the players jogged onto the field, Coach Frost grabbed the arm of his kicker, Kyle Sharp. Kyle's body was trembling in fear.

"We just need a clean kick," Coach Frost said. "Right down the pipe. You got this!"

With his eyes as wide as saucers, the tiny ex-soccer player could only manage to sputter out a weak "Yes, sir."

Coach Frost forced conviction in his voice, but the pit in his stomach felt what was coming.

The buzz of the crowd grew deafening. It'd been a long time since the Aviators had claimed a championship for their hometown, and people were hungry for something to celebrate.

The referee placed the ball at the line of scrimmage and blew his whistle. The final play of regulation had begun.

Kyle lined himself up like he had done hundreds of times before, but this was different. He felt the weight of thousands of eyes penetrating the back of his neck. His heart jittered. His feet were heavy.

He didn't want to let down the fans and the community.

But most of all, he was terrified of disappointing Coach Frost and his teammates. Despite being a senior who'd been on the team for three years, he still felt like an outsider. This was it—his time to show he belonged.

The cold November air turned Kyle's deep breaths into thick clouds of mist. The buzz of the crowd started to grow quiet.

Inhale, exhale. Inhale, exhale. He signaled that he was ready.

The snap spiraled backward into the waiting hands of the holder.

Kyle set, then he drove off his left foot.

THUMP!

The ball soared. The crowd held its breath. Coach Frost froze.

Kyle's kick drifted...wide left.

Just like that, the season was over.

CHAPTER 2

THE WINNING FORMULA

COACH FROST WOKE up to the buzzing of his alarm after another choppy night of sleep. It'd been more than a month since the playoffs, but Coach Frost still replayed the moment over and over again like a bad movie.

He could handle losing when he felt like his team had given all they had. But the feeling of giving away another playoff game was enough to make him sick.

The disappointment was becoming routine: outstanding regular season performances capped by embarrassing losses in the playoffs. The community was starting to get sick of it.

This loss, though, stung even more than the others. It wasn't just the fact that the Aviators had lost in the final moments—it was *how* it had happened. The leaders he'd counted on all season seemed to disappear in the toughest moments.

The look on Kyle's face as he lined up for the kick had made it clear that he didn't want to be out there. He wasn't ready to rise to the occasion—he was *just trying not to fail*. Something in his program was missing, and he had no idea what it was.

Most off-seasons, Coach Frost traveled his usual circuit of offensive and defensive clinics. This year, he knew he needed to dive deeper than just X's and O's. He'd decided to meet with leaders he respected to see if he could understand what was missing in his program.

Frost drove out to meet Grant Hartman, the president of a local car dealership.

Over the years, the dealership had grown from a small family startup to an industry giant, and Coach Frost wanted to know how he'd made the jump.

Sitting at a coffeehouse table one Saturday afternoon, Hartman told him.

"One person who really helped my thinking was Cooper Williams, the old football coach. He happens to be speaking to our company Monday morning. How about you come by?"

Coach Frost knew all about Cooper and the success he'd had at Coolridge High School. In fact, Coach Frost had adopted his entire defensive system years earlier and loved it. It was a promising lead. *Maybe the old football coach had more to teach him.*

Monday morning, Coach Frost emerged through the dealership doors into a chatty crowd of suit-wearing professionals. Standing there in his Westlake hoodie, he couldn't help but feel out of place. He quickly settled into a chair in the back and opened his notebook.

A few minutes later, Mr. Hartman walked up to the podium and adjusted the microphone.

"Good morning, everyone! Glad you all could make it. Today, we welcome an incredible football coach, a special leader, and a remarkable human being. As head coach of Coolridge High, Cooper Williams broke boundaries. Now, Cooper's incredibly humble, and he hates when I mention this," Hartman said, looking offstage, "but this guy went 112–7 as head coach. He won five straight state championships over a seventy-game winning streak. But what's most impressive is Cooper's impact off the field. Since wrapping up his coaching career, Cooper has been dedicated to lending his leadership skills to organizations around the world—and today, that's us.

Cooper, we're so happy to have you with us. We're committed to building a championship team here at Hartman, and we can't wait to learn from you. Everybody, give a warm welcome to Mr. Cooper Williams!"

Cooper positioned himself in the center of the stage with a big display screen illuminating behind him. He was tall, with the lean strength of a coach who'd stayed active in retirement. You could see his big, beaming grin from a mile away.

"Thank you, Mr. Hartman. I'm really grateful to be here with all of you today.

With a lot of help, I was blessed to lead one of the winningest programs in the country. But even though we won a lot, we didn't focus solely on winning."

Sitting in the back, Coach Frost was puzzled. *Winning doesn't matter? To the coach with the longest win streak in our state's history?*

"Now, I understand this is real life. Outcomes matter. Winning matters. Profits matter. But we understood early on that those things were not entirely in our control," Cooper said, as if he had picked up on Coach Frost's confusion.

"Instead of focusing on *those results*, we relentlessly focused on the factors *driving those results*. There was never a 'secret' to our success. But there *was* a system.

Remember this—when it comes to getting results:

Bad leaders have hopes.
Average leaders have quotes.
Elite leaders have *systems*.

At Coolridge, our system was called The Winning Formula."

Words popped up on the big screen behind him. Cooper pointed to them.

The Winning Formula = People + Culture + Preparation + Execution

Coach Frost surveyed the crowd—everybody was locked in. You could tell this was second nature for Cooper.

He clicked a button and the word "PEOPLE" appeared on the screen.

"Everything starts with your people. Bricks don't build championships. People do.

You aren't successful here at Hartman because of this beautiful building. You are successful because of the drive, grit, and determination of the people right here in this room.

Businesses don't get better. People do.

Elite organizations don't take their people for granted. They intentionally focus on them. They *develop* their people. They *listen* to their people. They *love* their people.

Ultimately, the best organizations know it's the people who drive results.

When we were most successful on the football field, it wasn't about winning football games. It was about showing up every day and giving your best for the guy next to you because you cared about them so much. When that happens, the scoreboard takes care of itself."

The word "CULTURE" popped up on the screen. Cooper continued.

"'Culture' is a buzzword that is overused but underdefined. We simply define culture as 'how we do things.'

How we communicate.
How we behave.
How we respond to adversity.
How we train.
How we recognize one another.

Great teams don't become great just because of *what* they do.
They become great because of *how* they do things.

Culture happens either by design or by default. It's born out of the collective beliefs and behaviors of all the people that make up an organization.

The vision of the culture may start from the top of the organization, but it comes to life through everybody underneath. You can have all the mission statements, signs, slogans, posters, and wristbands you want, but until *everyone* takes ownership of the culture, it will never fully come to life.

Every culture is perfectly designed to get the results it is currently getting. And when I say 'results,' it's beyond just profit margins. It's everything. Employee engagement. Community impact. Guest experience. Employee morale. All of this reflects your culture."

Cooper hit the button again, and the word "PREPARATION" flashed onto the screen.

"John Wooden once said, 'When opportunity comes, it's too late to prepare.' The organizations on top of the mountain didn't simply fall there. Their success we see from the outside is the result of countless hours behind the scenes, in the dark. Every battle is won before it is fought. If you don't roll up your sleeves and do the work in the dark—when your opportunity comes, you won't be ready to take advantage. Your work ethic must exceed your expectations."

As he finished, the last word popped up on the screen: "EXECUTION."

"Now, everyone within a culture has a role they are responsible for executing. And many of those roles aren't flashy or exciting. They are simply *hard work*.

But the moment one person doesn't execute, the entire team takes a hit. Everybody has to hold the rope and pull in the same direction.

The New England Patriots are one of the winningest franchises in all of sports. You know what one of the only signs in their facility said? 'Do Your Job.'"

Cooper paused.

"Culture is dynamic. It's alive. And it's either growing or it's dying. It's either getting better or it's getting worse. Culture never stays the same.

Don't just try to sustain your culture. Build it. Grow it. Make it better.

Because the moment you think you have it all figured out, you allow complacency and entitlement to sink their claws into your culture. And that is when things start to crumble.

Everybody wants a championship culture, but most aren't willing to do what a championship culture requires. My charge for everybody here today: take ownership of your culture, and do something every day to grow it."

As Cooper walked offstage, Coach Frost couldn't believe what he had heard. He'd felt like Cooper was speaking directly to him.

After the event ended, Coach Frost waited until the final person had left to approach Cooper and thank him for his time. They got to talking. Coach Frost told him a bit about his program, where he came from. Cooper mentioned he had recently moved into the area.

Coach Frost had an idea. *It may be a long shot*, he thought, *but what do I have to lose?*

"Cooper? You know, I would love to have you join our staff this season. In any capacity you want. I want your help in growing our leadership, our culture. Would you be interested in that at all?"

Cooper smiled and responded. "Let me get your number. You may have asked me at just the right time."

CHAPTER 3

GREAT LEADERS ARE GREAT LISTENERS

THE NEXT MORNING, Coach Frost woke up to a text from Cooper.

I'm in. Let's meet in your office this afternoon.

For the first time since the playoff loss, Coach Frost was filled with hope.

Coach Frost's office at Westlake High sat adjacent to the weight room. It was spacious, containing a wide desk, a few whiteboards, and a large circular table for group conversations.

At 1:00 p.m. sharp, he heard a knock and the door popped open.

"Coach Frost?"

"Cooper!" Frost hopped out of his chair and met him at the door. Cooper may have been retired from football, but with his physique, he looked like he could still suit up at quarterback.

"Welcome to Westlake. It's so great to have you in here."

As he shook Cooper's hand, Coach Frost grinned.

"Where do we start?" Coach Frost asked as they both got seated. "You want a playbook? Personnel sheet?"

Cooper laughed and leaned forward. "Slow down, Coach. Let me get a little more familiar with how you do things around here."

Coach Frost paused, his grin fading a bit.

"Let me ask you this," Cooper said, "What do your players think about your current culture?"

"My players?" Coach Frost's eyes darted away from Cooper's. "I guess we don't really talk about it."

"You don't get feedback from your guys?" Cooper asked.

"I mean, we have end-of-the-year meetings, but we usually discuss the individual player, you know? Their strengths, their weaknesses. Their goals for next year. Never really about the whole *culture*."

"Coach, it's impossible to know what's going wrong with the team when you don't know what's going on *within* the team," Cooper said, pulling a notebook out of his bag. "I was going to wait until next week—but since we got guys in the weight room right now, why don't we get some of them in here and hold a listening session?"

Coach Frost shuddered at the mention of a listening session. The thought of hearing what his players really thought—*especially* only a month after one of their most disappointing defeats—wasn't something he looked forward to. But he couldn't let Cooper down this soon.

"Couldn't hurt," he replied, trying to hide his nerves. "I'll go round them up."

Minutes later, he returned with four of the team's most crucial guys: the reliable center Kade Nelson; thick-necked middle linebacker Trey Rostrum; star quarterback Easton Hayes; and Easton's outspoken sidekick, the receiver Sebastian Martinez.

"Take a seat," Coach Frost said to the incoming players. "I want to introduce you to someone who's gonna be helping us out this season. This is Cooper Williams. I'm sure you've heard of him. Brilliant coach."

Cooper spoke. "Great to meet you all. What I want to do today is get your feelings on the team culture and the leaders within it. I know you are a talented football team, but from what I hear, something is keeping you from executing in the toughest moments."

He surveyed the four faces. "Who wants to start?"

The room was dead silent. The players looked at each other, wondering who would go first. It was clear to see they were scared to speak up in front of each other. Even Sebastian, whose mouth moved a mile a minute, was uncharacteristically quiet.

"Anyone?" Cooper prodded. "Sebastian. What do you think is holding this team back?"

The skinny receiver sat up straight and responded. "I just think so many players are selfish. Worried about their stats. *Their* starting spot. *Their* scholarship."

His words shocked the other players. For as long as they had known him, Sebastian had been the exact player he described.

Easton cut in. "I think that a lot of times, everyone's on different pages. The coaches, the players, everyone. Our communication sucks."

"Gotcha," Cooper responded. "And how does that impact you as players?"

"It makes it hard to play as a team, honestly. Like what Sebastian said, everybody is focused on themselves, in their own silos. They are not thinking about what's going on with their teammates," Easton said.

Kade jumped in. "I feel like I can do a thousand things right and never hear a word from my teammates or coaches—but I do one thing wrong and I never hear the end of it. It's exhausting."

Cooper turned to the quiet middle linebacker. "How about you, Trey? You haven't said anything. What's going on in your mind?"

Trey hesitated, keeping his gaze on the ground. He finally spoke up.

"It is hard to get better here, man. If you work your butt off, you get ripped on and labeled as a 'try-hard.' If you try to lead, people just say you are trying to suck up to the coaches." He paused and folded his arms.

"It's just easier to worry about yourself, not say anything, and fly under the radar."

The boys continued to share openly with Cooper over the next thirty minutes. Once the floodgates were open, concerns about the team's culture came tumbling out. While they shared, Coach Frost listened intently. After thanking the boys for their honesty, Cooper encouraged them to play vital roles in building a new and better culture.

For the next few hours, groups of players continued to pour in, encouraged by Cooper to finally say what was on their minds. By the end of it, Coach Frost was mentally exhausted.

After the final group left, Cooper turned to Coach Frost.

"Well, Coach—what'd you think?"

Coach Frost closed his notebook. "That was tough. It's just...a lot to take in. I didn't realize how they were feeling. If I'm being honest, it hurts to hear that."

Cooper nodded. "Before you can create a beautiful future, you must have the courage to confront the ugly reality. And that only happens when you intentionally start listening." He sat back down across the table.

"I have never worked with a team or an organization that doesn't have problems. Everyone has gaps. It's about developing leaders that solve those problems quickly and effectively. And that begins with listening.

Great leaders are great listeners. People won't care how much you *know* until they know how much you *care*. And the fastest way to show someone you care is by truly listening."

Cooper paused to let that sink in.

"There is nothing flashy about becoming a great listener. It doesn't happen by accident. You must commit to honing these skills. I mean, think about it. In school, we learned to write, speak, and read—but listening? When did we learn how to really listen?

We need your player leaders to be better listeners as well. But to do that, they need to see it modeled by someone they respect. Someone like you. That's why what you did today was so powerful."

"I appreciate that, Coop."

Cooper leaned over and put his hand on Coach Frost's shoulder to wrap up the conversation. Before he left, Coach Frost asked a question.

"Hey, Coop," Coach Frost said. "I'm curious about something. Why us? I mean, you could pretty much be working with any other organization and getting paid a lot more for your time."

Cooper responded with a smile.

"When I was sixteen years old, my mother passed away. She'd had a long battle with cancer. She was the rock of our family, and it crushed me. My dad did everything he could to raise me and my sisters, but it was a lot to deal with."

Cooper's eyes welled up with tears as he remembered.

"I had coaches devote themselves to helping me out when I needed it the most. And now, I'm here to do the same."

Cooper started walking toward the door before turning back to Coach Frost.

"Get some sleep—tomorrow, everything starts to change."

CHAPTER 4

WHO OWNS THE CULTURE?

EVEN THOUGH IT was only January, Coach Frost knew he didn't have any time to waste. The upcoming season would arrive in no time. So, less than a week after the listening sessions, Coach Frost assembled his entire program to meet Cooper.

Most of the players had grown up hearing about Cooper's success at Coolridge, and he hoped Cooper's presence would help his players overcome the sting of the tough playoff loss.

To allow space for everyone, Coach Frost scheduled the meeting in the auditorium. Once the team settled in, Coach Frost introduced Cooper and gave him the stage.

After a quick welcome, Cooper asked the group an important question.

"Who owns the culture of this program?"

His voice filled the auditorium.

The boys rustled in their seats. Eventually, most of their eyes landed on Coach Frost.

Cooper moved his gaze across the room. He pointed to the quarterback in the middle row. "What do you think, Easton?"

Easton glanced at Sebastian and smirked. "I guess Coach Frost."

"What about you?" Cooper prodded Kade.

"I don't know. I'd probably say Coach Frost too."

Cooper nodded and let the silence linger.

"Gentlemen, that belief is one of your greatest limiters."

Coach Frost admired the way Cooper could be direct and to the point while still delivering his message from a place of empathy and care.

"The direction of your culture may be set by your coaches, but it comes alive through the beliefs and the behaviors of everybody in this room. You all own the culture of this program. In the end, Coach Frost isn't the one playing in between the lines. It's you."

Cooper's penetrating stare and confident demeanor had the group mesmerized.

"A football coach once said," Cooper continued,

'On bad teams, nobody leads.
On average teams, coaches lead.
But on elite teams, players lead.'[1]

Judging from your answers, this team is average at best. Creating elite teams means developing players that choose ownership over excuses. It's starting with leaders that choose courage over fear."

Easton shifted around in his seat. He was starting to feel like Cooper was speaking directly to him.

"Player-led teams operate in a radically different way than coach-led teams," Cooper explained.

"Coach-led teams expect their coach to solve their issues.
Player-led teams figure things out and find solutions.

---

1 P. J. Fleck

Coach-led teams need their coach to motivate them daily.
Player-led teams find that motivation on their own.

Coach-led teams need their coach to hold them accountable.
Player-led teams hold each other accountable.

Coach-led teams like to blame others and hide behind excuses.
Player-led teams take 100 percent ownership."

Cooper paused and let his message resonate.

He continued. "A Navy SEAL once said, 'There are no bad teams. Just bad leaders.' The results that this team gets *tomorrow* are a representation of what the leaders in this room are willing to do *today*.

Too often I find leaders getting caught looking out the window, blaming outside circumstances for the results they are getting.

They say, 'Well, the reason we haven't gotten over the hump is…

We can't make an extra point.
Our facilities aren't the biggest.
Coach doesn't call the right plays.
We don't have the nicest equipment.
Other players aren't working as hard as I am.'

The truth is, you won't find your biggest challenge looking out the window. You'll find it looking in the mirror.

You might be able to fool others, but you can't cheat the person in the mirror. Deep down, you know whether you have cut corners, or if you gave everything that you had.

In our society, blaming and making excuses is easy. Taking 100 percent ownership is hard.

Casting blame and making excuses is like a virus. It's contagious. So be different. Be a team that takes collective ownership.

And collective ownership means not just one person in here—not just two people in here—but *all of you* committing to taking ownership, eliminating excuses, and being the architects of the culture that you want to create."

Cooper paused.

"This is an opportunity to build your own house."

After Cooper thanked the group, Coach Frost returned, shook Cooper's hand, and addressed the team.

"I want you all to know that this is something I am completely committed to growing in myself personally. This conversation can't stop here today. That's why we're creating a leadership council to give you all an opportunity for more ownership over this culture. On your way out, cast your vote for a member of your position group to represent you in these conversations."

The boys filled out their papers and handed them in as they walked out. Coach Frost stood by the door fist-bumping the players as they left. He didn't know where this was going, but he couldn't help but enjoy the positive momentum.

CHAPTER 5

THE TWIN THIEVES

THE FOLLOWING SATURDAY morning, the Aviators held their first Leadership Council meeting in Coach Frost's classroom. The team had selected nine players as leaders that would help build the foundation of a better culture.

The setup of the classroom was different than usual. Instead of its normal collection of neat rows, Cooper and Coach Frost formed a circle of chairs and positioned themselves on opposite ends. They welcomed the players with a smile as they entered.

Cooper had been clear that things needed to start on time, and Coach Frost closed the door at 9:00 a.m. sharp.

Everybody except quarterback Easton Hayes was on time. Just a minute late, Easton knocked on the door hoping he would get a free pass. Cooper allowed him to enter because it was the first meeting, but everybody understood the message going forward. Being on time was the standard.

"You are all here because you're leaders," Cooper began, moving his gaze from player to player. "Whether you believe it or not—the kids on this team look up to you. You are the most influential people on this team. Now is your opportunity to leverage that influence to grow this culture.

I've worked with a lot of different businesses, teams, and organizations over the past several years, and one thing is certain: there's no *perfect* culture. Every culture has issues, every culture has challenges. But a culture becomes *elite* when it has leaders who solve these problems effectively and efficiently.

In average cultures, people avoid the main issues. They leave the biggest challenges 'under the table' and hope they will just go away. Elite cultures purposefully and relentlessly address the elephant in the room. They become great at putting everything—even the painful stuff—'on top of the table.'

In our listening sessions, you all did a great job of putting some of the challenges in this culture on top of the table. It's clear that you currently have very little trust and connection."

Cooper paused and then continued with a calm conviction. "Here's the challenge right now. You all and your coaches aren't running this program—the Twin Thieves are.

The Twin Thieves are robbing your culture from being the best version of itself."

Sebastian spoke up. "I don't get it. The Twin Thieves? What are those?"

Cooper smiled. He knew he had their attention now. "Please take the blank piece of paper that was on your seat when you walked in, and answer this question:

What holds you back from being the best leader you can be?

Answer this without writing your name on it. I want you to be completely honest," Cooper explained. "Once you're done, crumple up your paper into a ball and throw it in the middle of the circle."

After all the papers were thrown into the middle, each player picked up a random answer and shared it with the group.

"What others think and say about me."
"Screwing up in front of everyone."
"People making fun of me behind my back."
"Being scared that if I try to lead, others won't follow."
"Being alone."
"Not being talented enough to take a leadership role."
"Fear of letting people down."

"Being called a Try Hard."

"Scared of failing, it is easier to play it safe and not say anything."

The mood grew heavier as Cooper put the players' fears on top of the table. It was the first time many of them felt comfortable being vulnerable in front of their teammates. Cooper let these powerful responses sink in.

"That right there—that is the *Twin Thieves*. The Twin Thieves are the fear of failure and the fear of judgment. And they are the biggest thieves in America right now.

We call them twins because they often look like the same thing. And it can be really easy to confuse the two. When people say they're scared of failure, they usually mean they're scared of the judgment that comes *after* the failure."

The team was silent, absorbing Cooper's wisdom.

"We call them thieves because they can rob us blind if we allow them to," Cooper added. "What are some things the fear of failure and the fear of judgment can rob us of?"

They all thought for a second. Surprisingly, Trey piped up first.

"I guess I'd say opportunities. If you're scared of failing at something, you're probably not gonna try it."

"Good. What else?"

"I think it can rob us of our growth," Kade volunteered. "Our potential. Like Trey said, you can't keep improving if you're scared of failing and being judged."

Sebastian jumped in. "Confidence. Yeah, I think they could definitely rob us of our confidence."

"Absolutely!" Cooper responded. "Just imagine. What opportunities have the Twin Thieves robbed from you because you were just too scared to simply step into the arena? What would you have tried if the fear of failure and the fear of judgment weren't standing in your way? How would your life be different?" Cooper asked.

"How would this culture be different if the Twin Thieves weren't lurking around every corner?"

Cooper paused again and leaned forward in his chair. "Right now, this culture is built on fear. You can't consistently win if you're just playing *not* to lose."

Out of nowhere, Easton's insecurities got the best of him.

"Well, it seems to be working just fine," he said, shrugging. "We're 22-4 with me at quarterback. Kinda seems like fear is an excellent motivator."

Cooper took an intentionally long pause and turned to Easton. The confrontation made everyone uncomfortable.

"Well, Easton, that may be true in the regular season. But how has that mindset been working out in the biggest moments of the playoffs?"

The room was silent. Even Easton understood the truth in Cooper's reflection.

"A few years back," Cooper shared. "Google conducted a research project to figure out one question: What makes effective teams?"

Cooper paused. "Their research lasted over two years and included more than 200 interviews. They studied over 250 attributes that impacted the 180-plus teams they had within their company.

Surprisingly, one attribute rose far above all the others." Cooper scanned the group. "Any idea what it was?" he asked.

The group shook their heads.

"Psychological safety." Cooper responded with a smile, knowing it was a new term.

"Basically, they found that the number one thing driving great teams is developing an environment that rises above the Twin Thieves. A team where people know they can take risks without being ridiculed, exposed, or embarrassed."

Cooper paused before wrapping up. "A culture built on fear might produce immediate results, but to become a transformational, championship culture that stands the test of time, there has to be a major shift in the way you do things.

A shift from focusing on *wins* to focusing on *people.*
A shift from authoritarian leadership to servant leadership.
A shift from disconnection to connection.
A shift from coaches steering the ship to *players* taking the wheel.
And most importantly, a shift from fear to *love.*

The greatest barrier holding this team back isn't out there somewhere. It's right here in this room," Cooper said.

"Now—it's up to all of us to defeat it."

CHAPTER 6

THE SURVIVAL BRAIN

THE NEXT MORNING, Coach Frost was thrilled. The first Leadership Council meeting had gone better than he'd expected. However, he still had questions about the ideas that Cooper had brought up.

"Can't we just block out the Twin Thieves? Or eliminate them somehow?" Coach Frost asked.

"That is a great question." Cooper responded with a smile. "And that would be nice—if it were possible!

"Many, many years ago," Cooper started to explain, "like way back in caveman days—what do you think our brain was most concerned about? What was its top priority?"

Coach Frost shrugged. "Survival, I guess."

"Exactly!" Cooper continued. "And to survive better, we learned that fitting in and being accepted by a tribe of people was crucial. Why is that?"

"Well, there's strength in numbers," Coach Frost responded quickly.

"Right!" Cooper said, nodding his head. "Unless you're Jason Bourne or a Jedi Knight, your chances of surviving against wild animals, harsh temperatures, and treacherous conditions alone would be *slim to none.*

The most primal part of our brain—which I like to call the Survival Brain—learned that fitting in and being accepted by other people was crucial, because it could literally mean the difference between life or death.

So fear—specifically the fear of failure and the fear of judgment—became your Survival Brain's best strategy for keeping you safe.

And thousands of years ago, your Survival Brain was right. The Twin Thieves *were* effective at helping you survive.

But things have changed. These days, we don't need to escape saber-tooth tigers or hunt our own food. We aren't just hoping to *survive* anymore. We want to *thrive*. And the only way you can do that is by overcoming fear."

Cooper paused and swirled the coffee in his hand.

"Our brains have advanced in so many ways, but the tendencies of that old, outdated, fear-driven Survival Brain still remain. Today, our Survival Brain struggles to tell the difference between things that are actually *life-threatening* versus things that are just ego-threatening."[2]

Coach Frost spoke up, "What about the professional athletes or the big-time business owners that you work with? You are telling me they still experience the Twin Thieves?"

"Absolutely," Cooper said, smiling. "Many of them spent years learning that emotions like fear and anxiety aren't a weakness. They're more like a compass, pointing you in the right direction, away from obstacles.

The best in the world still feel fear when they're pushing their comfort zones. But they've learned to embrace the Twin Thieves, trust their training, and *do it anyway*.

You aren't alone or broken for having fears of failure or of judgment. The Twin Thieves are biological. But if you're constantly trying to fight them or block them out, they *will* break you down."

Cooper paused and asked, "Have you ever noticed what happens when you try really hard to block out or eliminate the Twin Thieves?"

---

2 Peter Crone quote

Coach Frost smiled, knowing the answer intuitively. "They get stronger."

"It's almost unfair," Cooper responded. "But whatever you resist persists."

"So if we aren't trying to eliminate the Twin Thieves, what do we do?" Coach Frost asked.

"You have to relate to them better," Cooper responded.

Coach Frost looked confused. Cooper scooted forward and explained.

"In order to transcend the Twin Thieves, you will have to approach fear differently than how most people approach fear.

Instead of fighting the Twin Thieves, embrace them. The insecure ego inside of us doesn't want to be healed. It wants to be held.[3] For example, when a young child is tired and has a breakdown, yelling at them doesn't help. Pulling them in and holding them does. This is the same way you embrace the nervous, scared, or insecure part of you.

Instead of blindly believing the Twin Thieves, question all of your thoughts. By questioning the truth of your thoughts, you will learn that the Twin Thieves are fueled by lies based on your deepest insecurities.

Instead of running away from the Twin Thieves, go toward them. When you think of the moments you are most proud of, fear usually preceded them. That's because the Twin Thieves tend to show up around the things you care the most about.

Getting back to the culture here, though," Cooper said, refocusing the conversation, "how do you think the Twin Thieves can hold an entire group back?"

Coach Frost sat in thought for a second. "I guess that when people operate according to the Twin Thieves, all they want to do is fit in with everybody

---

3 Peter Crone quote

else. They keep people from pushing themselves—*really* pushing themselves—because they're scared they might screw up or look bad."

"Exactly!" Cooper responded. He was visibly excited with Coach Frost's progress and understanding.

"Players hold back and cover up their greatness because they are too worried about being called a try-hard or a suck-up. And if nobody is willing to stand out and be different, we get average effort, average commitment, and average fight. This all results in average results.

I have never met a successful person who wasn't a try-hard. I have never witnessed a high-performing culture that did not recognize and embrace the try-hards."

Coach Frost clearly understood what Cooper was saying. Coach Frost replied, "You're making me think of one of my favorite quotes." He took out his phone and began reading.

> Playing small does not serve the world. There is nothing enlightened about shrinking so that other people won't feel insecure around you. We are all meant to shine, as children do. And as we let our own light shine, we unconsciously give other people permission to do the same. As we are liberated from our own fear, our presence automatically liberates others.

Coach Frost put his phone down, and Cooper nodded his head with a big smile.

"That nails it." Cooper replied. "The primal desire to fit in with the group will always be powerful. We just need to make sure that what our players want to fit in to is a culture of excellence. One that shines."

Cooper paused. "Ultimately, the teams that function out of fear will merely survive. But those that learn to dance with the Survival Brain, to embrace the Twin Thieves, and push themselves beyond what they thought was possible? That team will be unstoppable, Coach."

CHAPTER 7

THE COUNTERPUNCH TO FEAR

THE FOLLOWING WEDNESDAY, Cooper invited Coach Frost and the Leadership Council members to his house for dinner. It was only mid-February, but the group of leaders seemed to have more chemistry than ever before. Everybody was excited to see how improving their culture could help them in the season ahead.

As the guests arrived, they trickled down into the basement to talk before they ate. Cooper's walls were filled with snapshots from his coaching days. There were pictures of Cooper hugging his players, pictures of his players graduating, pictures of his coaching staff getting together. Half of the pictures didn't even have Cooper in them—it seemed like a perfect example of Cooper's love for his people.

Cooper caught Coach Frost in the middle of admiring the pictures.

"I was fortunate to be a part of many state championships, Coach. But let me tell you something. The trophies and rings collect dust, but these memories and these relationships will never fade."

"You must have had some real studs on those teams," Easton said from across the room, visualizing himself winning a championship himself someday.

Cooper smiled. "You bet we did. I have never seen a team win a championship without talent, but I have seen a lot of really talented teams *not* win a championship.

One of the secret ingredients is connection, Easton. Connected teams are powerful teams."

The boys spent a while prodding Cooper about his glory days. Eventually, Cooper led them to the table and got down to business.

"You have had a lot to think about over the past few days. What's one thing that you're wrestling with the most?"

Easton chuckled, shook his head, and thought for a minute. "Can we start with how you ended our last conversation? You said we needed to shift from fear to love."

Sebastian piggybacked off Easton's comment.

"Yeah, what do you mean? I already give our freshmen a lot of tough love. I got tough love all the time when I was a freshman, and now I get to pass that on."

Cooper gave his own chuckle. "Yeah, I used to give out a lot of *tough love* when I was a younger coach. But I learned the hard way that even though it works in the short term, constantly giving tough love without building strong relationships leads to long-term trust issues.

And I'll tell you one more thing—it feels a lot better to *give* tough love than it does to receive it," Cooper said with a smirk.

Cooper continued, "I learned the hard way that the key is to switch the words around. Love tough. Love must always come first in leadership."[4]

"So we should just let everything slide in our program?" Easton said. "Not have any accountability? Never tell people when they're screwing up?"

Cooper shook his head. "Love isn't about letting things slide. It's about setting high standards and consistently holding your teammates to those standards."

Easton shot up.

---

4 Trent Dilfer quote

"Okay, fine. Let's say we all love each other. What do you want us to do? Sit around, hold hands, and sing 'Kumbaya'? Football is a man's sport. We need to win games. There is no room for that soft stuff in our program."

"There is nothing soft about love," Cooper said calmly. "And if you're uncomfortable using the word 'love'—try replacing it with 'care.'

It's not about hating the person across from you, it's about working your absolute hardest because you love the person next to you."

Easton was silent, the gears in his head turning. It was a radical shift from how the team had always operated.

Cooper looked over to Coach Frost, "Coach, you have two daughters, right?"

"Yes, sir. Rae is six and Marie is four. Best things that ever happened to me," Coach replied.

"What would happen if someone broke into your house in the middle of the night and tried to hurt your two angels?" Cooper asked.

The question was sharp, and everyone looked at Coach Frost. There was an intensity in his eyes that they hadn't seen before.

"Well, they probably wouldn't make it out the door alive. Nobody hurts my daughters."

"Exactly! Now, that is not because you *hate* the individual who broke into your house—you don't even know that person. It's because you *love* your daughters.

Love inspires tenacity. Love is the *furthest* thing from soft."

Cooper turned and pointed to a sign behind him bearing a quote.

It read: *The true soldier fights not because he hates what is in front of him, but because he loves what is behind him. ~ G.K. Chesterton*

"When you can create a culture where people truly care about each other, you won't need so much *tough* love.
The team will fight *for* each other, not *with* each other.
They'll hold each other accountable to be their best.
They'll work their hardest—because the last thing they want to do is let each other down.
One of the most important skills of a leader is the ability to move the human heart. You don't do that through fear—you do that through love."

Just then, Cooper's wife called down to let them know dinner was ready.

Before they all got up, Cooper had one more thing to say.

"Fear has been driving this culture, fellas. And you know what the most powerful counterpunch to fear is? *Love.*"

CHAPTER 8

SERVANT LEADERSHIP

THE FOLLOWING SATURDAY after dinner at Cooper's, the Leadership Council came back together. The team's progress was harder for Coach Frost and the players to recognize, but Cooper could see that they were making big leaps in understanding the power of strong cultures.

Once everyone was settled into their seats in the large circle, Cooper took his place at the front of the room.

"Thank you for being here this morning, gentlemen. Today, I want to have a conversation about leadership.

Leadership is one of the most-studied topics in the entire world. Ironically, it's also one of the *least-understood* topics in the world."

Cooper paused and gestured to a question he had written on the board.

"Let's start with this. Who is the best leader in your life, and why?" Cooper asked.

He gave the team some time to think before asking for a volunteer to start. Surprisingly, it was Kade, the only junior in the room, who raised his hand first.

"All right, Kade, you start, and let's go around the circle."

"For me, it's my dad. He has taught me so many things in my life, like how to treat others with respect and how to work hard for the things I want."

The rest of the group shared their answers. When Easton's turn came, it took him a second to answer. He didn't really like talking about this stuff.

"I would say my mom. I mean, everyone here knows how my dad is. Honestly, the only thing he cares about is my football career and work," Easton continued. "My mom is basically like a single mother. She sacrifices so much for our family. She even quit her job when I was younger just to take care of us."

After Easton was done, Sebastian followed. "Personally, it's Coach Hastings, my position coach. He just…*understands* me, you know? I don't always like him in the moment because he demands a lot. But looking back on the past couple of years, in my toughest moments, he was always there."

They continued around the circle. The last player to go was Trey.

"I wouldn't be here without my grandma. She took my siblings and me in when we were younger and raised us like a mother. She is sixty-eight years old and still works two jobs. She's just amazing," he said with a smile.

"I appreciate everyone sharing," Cooper said to the entire group. "There's a lot that these people have in common as great leaders, but two things clearly stand out.

First, one myth of leadership is that you must be famous to have an impact. I have never heard of any of these people, yet you all look at them as the most influential leaders you know.

And, second, they are all servants."

Cooper turned to Easton with a smile. "Easton, did you know that your mom is your servant?"

Easton got a huge smirk on his face. Chuckling, he said "Yeah, she is!"

All the players laughed. Cooper grinned and gave them a few seconds to enjoy the comment before continuing.

"Easton, do you always like your mom? *Every* minute of *every* day?"

"No way," Easton responded, raising his eyebrows with a smile.

"Why is that? When are there moments when you don't necessarily *like* your mom?" Cooper asked.

Easton thought for a minute. "I mean, obviously I don't like it when she grounds me. Or when she makes me do things I don't want to do."

"Hmm. So you don't like it when she holds you accountable? When she pushes you to be the best version of yourself? Why do you think she does all that?" Cooper asked.

Easton adjusted himself in his chair. "I guess it's because she loves me and cares about me. She just wants me to succeed."

"Bingo," Cooper exclaimed. He looked back at the rest of the boys.

"What you just described in your answers is the highest form of leadership: servant leadership.

Don't confuse servant leadership with being subservient. I don't think any of the people you mentioned are pushovers.

They give you what you need—which isn't always what you want.
They have hard conversations.
They hold you accountable.
They push you outside of your comfort zone.

And they do all of those things from their heart, because they care about you."

Cooper stood up and made his way to the whiteboard. He drew two pyramids side-by-side, with levels of hierarchy inside them. He wrote "Freshmen" on the bottom and "Coaches" and "Seniors" on the top two levels.

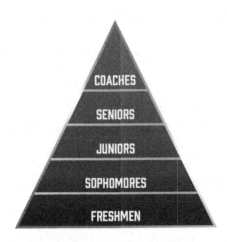

Cooper turned to the group. "*This*," he said, pointing at the first pyramid, "this is how most programs and organizations operate. These cultures are built on the belief that the underclassmen are there to serve the upperclassmen. The inexperienced serve the experienced. The players play for the coaches. The employees work for the CEO.

But if you want to grow this culture and become the best versions of yourself, you need to start by flipping the pyramid." Cooper pointed to the second pyramid.

The second triangle was upside down. This time, "Coaches" and "Seniors" were written on the *bottom* of the inverted pyramid, with "Freshmen" on the top.

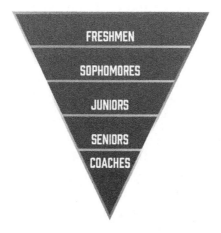

"In transformational cultures, that paradigm gets flipped on its head.

The coaches serve the players.
The upperclassmen serve the underclassmen.
The seniors pick up the field and the locker room.
The seniors give the freshmen rides home after practice.
The seniors put their arm around the underclassmen and reassure them everything will be okay."

Cooper paused. "Collectively, we need to intentionally look for opportunities to *serve each other*."

This was Easton's last straw.

"No way! I paid my dues as a freshman. We did whatever the upperclassmen said. Ask Seb or Trey. Now it's time for these freshmen to experience the same thing. It's how this whole thing works."

All of the seniors in the room nodded their heads in agreement.

"Can anyone tell me the definition of insanity?" Cooper asked.

"Doing the same thing over and over and expecting different results," Kade responded.

"Exactly, Kade." Cooper smiled. "You all agreed things need to change. Now, in order to get places you have never been, you have to do things you have never done," Cooper responded with a firm voice. "And sometimes that means letting go of old traditions that no longer support your vision.

You all are here because you are the most influential people in this culture. And when the most influential people become the hardest workers, show up early, stay late, truly care about their teammates, and aren't afraid to pick up the broom to sweep the sheds, suddenly the uncool becomes the cool thing to do."

For the next twenty-five minutes, the boys took the idea of servant leadership and transformed it into a list of behaviors they were willing to commit to.

It would be a big change from the traditional way of doing things. But deep down, everybody knew things needed to change. Even Easton was feeling the pull—though it all seemed unnecessary to him at the start, things were starting to click in his head.

Maybe it's time to make a change, he thought.

CHAPTER 9

THE COCOON CUTTER

A FEW DAYS later, Cooper joined Coach Frost for a weight room session and could tell he had a lot on his mind. News about the Aviators' culture shift started to spread after Cooper challenged the seniors to serve the underclassmen.

Reluctantly, Coach Frost opened up to Cooper about what was on his mind.

"At first, the idea of change was exciting. I am committed to this process, but personally, I really struggle with change. Heck, I have been using the same coffee mug for the last eighteen years.

In the last couple days, I've already noticed a number of our coaches and players are resistant to the change. They'd rather keep doing things like we've always done them. And sometimes, I know what they mean. I mean, it's not like things are completely broken. We *have* won a lot of games over the years."

Cooper listened to Coach Frost intently before responding. "You are right. You have won a lot of games here. You could even say your program has a target on its back.

The reality is, sometimes targets get hit. But the toughest targets to hit are moving ones. That's why we must keep our target moving by evolving and bettering our best every day."

Coach Frost nodded along. The idea of bettering their best resonated with him.

Cooper continued, "Most people avoid change because they don't like the struggle that goes with it. Changing requires you to confront the Twin Thieves. To change, you must step into the unknown and away from the old ways of always doing things.

Great leaders and elite cultures are constantly evolving."

Cooper paused to make sure that Coach Frost understood. Then he asked, "Did Steve Jobs and his team at Apple sit around a table in 2001 and say, 'This iPod that spins is really cool, let's just stick with this'?

Of course not. Apple is elite because they are constantly changing, constantly evolving.

Unfortunately, a lot of people and organizations would rather stay comfortable and get worse instead of embracing discomfort to get better.

Blockbuster Video once owned over 9,000 video-rental stores in the United States. But in 2010, they had to file for bankruptcy because they failed to evolve with competitors like Netflix. The internet didn't kill Blockbuster. The company's inability to change did.

In 1996, Kodak dominated the photography industry and was the fifth-most-valuable brand in the world. They had over two-thirds of the global market share and employed over 145,000 people. When the industry went digital, Kodak actually created the first digital camera. But its investors were too afraid to launch the product. So they never did. As Kodak watched the world embrace digital photography, they filed for bankruptcy in 2012.

Some people don't like change because of the risk of failure. But the real risk is *not* changing."

Cooper could still sense Coach Frost's concern about his seniors.

"I know it's hard to watch people you care about struggle. But without productive struggle, there is no growth. As leaders, we can't be cocoon cutters."

Coach Frost looked perplexed.

"Let me explain with a story," Cooper said.

"There was once an old man sitting on his porch. As he sipped his morning coffee, something on the ground caught his eye. It was moving. Looking closer, he realized it was a cocoon.

Watching it struggle, the kind old man decided to help the cocooned butterfly escape. So he went into his house and grabbed a tiny pair of scissors. He bent down on one knee and gently cut the cocoon open without harming the butterfly.

And soon after—the butterfly died."

Coach Frost paused dramatically.

"You know why? The butterfly simply wasn't prepared for the world outside. It wasn't strong enough to fly. It's the process of struggling out of the cocoon that strengthens the butterfly. If it doesn't have the opportunity to grow through adversity, it never will.

If this culture is going to become transformational, we must shift our perspective and understand that *struggle strengthens us*.

Change is inevitable, but growth is optional."

CHAPTER 10

STARFISH STORY

COOPER LOVED THE pace at which the Aviators were changing and growing. However, over the years, he had learned that fast change could also bring out more fear and self-doubt. He could tell Trey was one player that seemed to be struggling.

The legend of Trey Rostrum began in middle school, when he was a twelve-year-old benching 230 pounds. He was the rare breed of player whose work ethic matched his incredible talent. Three years later, he was a freshman taking first-team reps for the Aviators.

While no one could diminish his work ethic, Trey wasn't the most vocal leader. And after Thursday's weight room workout ended, Cooper caught him sitting in the corner alone. He could tell something was on Trey's mind, but he wasn't sure Trey would let him in.

"Trey! Nice work today. You really got after it," Cooper told him with a proud smile.

"Thanks, Mr. Williams. Not a bad workout," Trey replied.

There was a long pause.

"What's going on, Trey? It seems like something's up."

Trey shook his water bottle nervously and took a sip.

"Honestly, Mr. Williams, I sorta feel like I don't belong on the Leadership Council. I mean, I work hard, I do my job on the field, but the thought of leading others feels like such a big weight on my shoulders. I don't know if I have what it takes."

"Why's that?" Cooper asked.

"It's just—Easton and Sebastian, they're these outgoing guys that everyone likes. It seems like people just want to follow them." Trey paused and took another sip.

"And then I think about the linebackers we've had in the past. How am I supposed to live up to them?"

Cooper nodded, absorbing Trey's words.

"Trey, you remember the Twin Thieves, right? Well, I didn't mention another sneaky thief. *Comparison.* Comparison from a place of fear is the thief of all joy. It feeds your mind with *lies.*

Lies like, 'I can't be a leader. I'm nothing like Martin Luther King Jr. or Oprah Winfrey or LeBron James. Who am I to lead?'

Most people don't have the courage to lead because they don't feel like they're *enough.* They start to believe the lies like...

I'm not smart enough.
I'm not experienced enough.
I'm not popular enough.
I'm not talented enough.
I'm not loud enough.

When these lies go unchecked, it's easy for them to get ingrained in your mind. And before long, you believe it's the truth."

Trey looked up at Cooper.

"Trey, *you are enough.* And you have what it takes to be a leader already. Let me tell you one of my favorite leadership stories.

There was once an old man out on his daily walk down the beach. In the distance, he saw a young boy—he was bending down, picking something up, and throwing it back in the water. The old man was confused. As he continued his walk, he noticed that the tides were low. He noticed hundreds—if not thousands—of starfish had been left behind on the beach. The abandoned starfish were flapping around in the sand, desperately searching for water.

When the old man approached the boy, he realized what the young boy was doing—returning the starfish to their home in the water.

The cynical old man walked up to the boy and asked, 'What are you doing? Why are you wasting your time? There are thousands of starfish here. You're never going to make a difference.'

Smiling, the young boy bent down, picked up another starfish, and gently tossed it into the water. Then he looked up at the old man and said, 'Well, I made a *difference* to that one.'

The mindset of the old man was: Why even try? What's the point? You are never going to change the world. You are never going to make a difference. But the young boy knew that while he may not change the *world*, he could change the world of at least one starfish."

Trey looked up at Cooper with a smile. Cooper continued.

"Most of us won't change the world like MLK or Oprah, but every day, we do have opportunities to change *someone's* world.

Every day, I want you to *intentionally* look for small opportunities to serve your teammates—eventually, you'll see that little by little, a little becomes a lot."

Cooper stood up. "Start small. Get the ball rolling. Find one opportunity to make a positive difference in a teammate's life. That'll get you some momentum."

Trey shook his hand. "Thanks, Mr. Williams."

"And can we stop with the whole 'Mr. Williams?' Call me Cooper," he said, flashing a grin.

Trey laughed. "Sounds good, Cooper," he said.

CHAPTER 11

10-80-10

"ARE YOU KIDDING me!"

Easton's voice echoed through the hallway as he approached Coach Frost's classroom for the Leadership Council meeting. Sebastian and Kade were at his sides. All three of them were glued to Easton's phone.

Cooper welcomed the boys and broke them from their trance. "Good morning! What's going on today?"

Easton turned his phone to Cooper and almost jumped at him. He was fuming.

"Can you believe this?" Easton extended the phone into Cooper's face. "State preseason rankings came out last night. We're number nine, which is a joke. But this guy is saying we're overrated. Look at this!"

On his phone, there was a social media post from local high school football blogger Shane Clark: "Honestly, nine is too high for a team as dysfunctional as the Aviators. Don't see them making the playoffs this year."

Cooper didn't say anything, but a smile broke across his face. Easton was annoyed by the joy Cooper seemed to have about the situation.

"Come in and take a seat. This works perfectly with what we're talking about today."

Once the boys settled into their spots, Cooper jumped in. "I would like to introduce a principle that you can lean into when you are battling the Twin Thieves as a leader, specifically when you are confronting the fear of judgment."

Cooper walked up to the whiteboard and wrote: "10-80-10."

"This is called the 10-80-10 principle." Cooper paused.

"Now, this is something that I've had to work on in my own career. Worrying about other people judging me, obsessing over what they thought—it's human nature.

Some people think that this feeling goes away when you become successful. It doesn't. The irony is, the Twin Thieves actually grow stronger and stronger if you don't learn to handle them.

As a leader, it's possible to do everything right and still be disliked. This can paralyze some people. It's one of the biggest reasons most people never step up to be a leader in the first place.

To survive as a leader, it's crucial to be intentional about which people get your energy."

Cooper pointed to the top "10%" on the whiteboard.

"This represents people that are all in on you. They know you. They trust you. They're ready to support you and your ideas no matter what."

Cooper pointed to the bottom "10%."

"However, there is a flip side to this group. A wise person I've learned from calls this group the 'Energy Vampires.'[5] These people are the fun-sponges who have the unique ability to suck the living energy out of any room. They seem to be addicted to negativity."

Cooper capped his marker and turned back to the group.

---

5 Jon Gordon quote

"Regardless of how effective you are as a leader, some people will never be happy with you. It can be perplexing sometimes, but there's a lot of reasons the Energy Vampires may try to tear you down.

They may dislike your decisions.
They may dislike your look.
They may dislike your skin color.
And they may just dislike you because everyone else seems to like you.

There's a ton of reasons why they might not like you. But most likely, it's really about their insecurities."

Cooper then pointed to the "80%."

"I like to call the middle 80 percent 'the bandwagoners.' They represent the majority of the culture, and they can be influenced by either of the '10-percenters.' As a leader, you have the opportunity to influence this large group every single day by giving them intentional focus and energy."

Cooper scanned the leadership group and then asked: "Looking at this breakdown, who do we tend to give the most time and energy to?"

Kade raised his hand. "For me, it's the bottom 10 percent. I'm constantly trying to please the Energy Vampires."

"Exactly, Kade. Why do you think that is?" Cooper asked.

Kade hesitated. "Honestly, I just don't want to disappoint people. It's something I want to work on, but I hate it when people don't like me."

"You are not the only one, Kade," Cooper said with a smile. "But trying to please this group is exhausting. It's like trying to pound a nail into the wall with your forehead. It's not effective—and it starts to give you a headache after a while."

The group laughed.

"Everyone wants to be liked. It's wired into our brain: *be accepted by the pack*.

However, the reality is that having *everyone* like you is impossible. And when we waste all our attention and energy on the Energy Vampires, we miss out on the opportunity to impact the vast majority of the group," Cooper explained.

Easton's hand shot up. "I hear ya, and it's easy for me to block out the Energy Vampires that I don't really know. But what about the guys on our team? Are you saying we just ignore them?"

"That's a great question," Cooper said, nodding. "As a leader, it's important to continue meeting the Energy Vampires with love and respect. Always get curious before you get judgmental. Find out the problem. A lot of times, you just don't know what they are going through.

But this is important: never argue with them. It's a no-win situation. Instead, when they are complaining, simply ask them a solution-focused question like 'How would you do things differently?'

If they say *nothing*, then it's obvious they're complaining just to complain.

But if they give you an idea you can use, it provides the opportunity to both improve your system *and* make them feel involved in decision making.

Don't allow the Energy Vampires to drain your energy just because they complain the loudest. Be intentional about who gets your focus and attention because it is the lifeblood of our culture."

CHAPTER 12

ABOVE THE LINE

THE PLAYERS' COMMITMENT continued to grow through the month of March. For the first time, the entire Leadership Council was on time for a Saturday morning meeting. No one wanted to be left outside when that door locked at 9:00 a.m.

"Good morning, everyone!" Cooper said. "Thanks for being on time. Today's going to require some heavy lifting, so I hope you're ready."

Cooper pointed at Easton's T-shirt that read "The Aviator Way."

For Coach Frost's entire tenure, the phrase signified what he hoped his program would be about. It was written everywhere: locker room walls, T-shirts, wristbands. The problem? No one on the team seemed to care. Over time, "The Aviator Way" became more of a running joke than a guiding compass for the team.

"What does the Aviator Way mean to you, Easton?" Cooper asked.

Easton looked around and smirked. Subtly imitating Coach Frost, he said: "Family. Preparation. Execution." The group held back their laughter. None of them could have explained the philosophy with any clarity, but they sure knew those three words.

"These core values look good, but it's clear they aren't anything more than just words." Cooper shared. "Today, we're changing that.

You all are here as a representation of your entire team." Cooper continued. "Every team is different. Every year is a restart. You know your teammates better than anybody. You know how they think. You know their strengths—and more importantly, you know their limitations."

The players listened closely, interested to see where this was going.

"Here's your challenge today," Cooper said. "You'll get fifteen minutes to bring these values to life."

Cooper motioned to the board where he had drawn a horizontal line.

"That line signifies the standard for what you will tolerate in this culture and what you don't. Above the Line behaviors are any specific actions that bring these three values to life. Below the Line behaviors are any actions that go against the values.

Your challenge today is to come up with specific examples of Above the Line and Below the Line behaviors."

Coach Frost and Cooper sat back and let the boys work. Before the timer ran out, the group wrapped up their collaboration.

"Sebastian, why don't you start?" Cooper asked. "What did you all come up with for Above the Line and Below the Line behaviors for 'Family?'"

"For Below the Line, we said blaming each other, complaining, and not taking the time to learn about new teammates." He paused. "For Above the Line, we said encouraging each other, having tough conversations, and holding each other accountable.

We were thinking back to our first session on the Twin Thieves. We can't beat them alone. We gotta come together to do that."

The group continued on and broke down each value. As the leaders shared, Cooper recorded their answers on the board.

"Great work, gentlemen," Cooper said. "But now—the real work begins. The truth is, this conversation was the easy part.

Think about it—how many teams start the season by saying:

Let's create a culture of more division, fear, and judgment.
We want to be less committed.
Let's get softer and weaker in the big moments.

You never hear this! Every team wants to win. Every team wants to grow. But are you willing to be the leaders this program needs to actually make that shift?

It's easy to support your teammates when you feel like it.
It's *hard* to be there for them when you've got so much on your own plate.

It's easy to sit around and talk about commitment.
But it's *hard* to be early for every workout.

It's easy to go all in when you are feeling great.
It's *hard* to do the extra rep when you're exhausted.

This isn't easy. And that is exactly why it can be our advantage."

The leaders nodded along. Cooper could tell they wanted things to change, but he'd been here before. He knew how challenging it was to actually execute on beliefs. But for now, this was progress.

CHAPTER 13

UBUNTU

PHWEEEET!

Coach Frost's whistle cut through the chilly March air, signaling the start of the offense vs. defense tug-of-war challenge. This was a yearly tradition that wrapped up the first spring workout. Coach Frost loved the intensity of the challenge. It was a great way for the new players to show their older teammates that they were ready to fight for them.

But Cooper watched the challenge with a different perspective. Ever since he arrived, Cooper could feel animosity and division between the offensive and defensive players. The tug-of-war challenge seemed to bring everything to a boiling point.

"You guys wanna go again? I bet Kade could sit out and we still win this thing," Sebastian barked at the defense after getting a win. "You guys are weak!"

Egos and frustration took over, and before long, it turned into a shoving match between offense and defense on the dew-covered grass outside the weight room.

"Bring it in!" Coach Frost's booming voice stopped the commotion. Reluctantly, the players assembled around him, divided—the defense on one side and the offense on the other.

As Coach Frost scanned the group, Cooper signaled to get his attention. Coach Frost readily turned it over to him to address the group.

"Let me ask you all a question." He spoke slowly, with conviction. The players' emotions seem to settle by the moment.

"What if you were the most talented, the most powerful, and the most intelligent player on this team, but all of a sudden, you discovered that you were alone, without your teammates? All of that talent, power, and intelligence wouldn't matter much, would it?"

Cooper scanned the group with a poised focus.

"Let me be clear here. I love intense competition within a team. Iron sharpens iron. *However,* we have issues when the Twin Thieves hijack us and turn competition into jealousy, selfishness, and infighting. That competition is no longer building us, it's breaking us.

I want you to really think. Does it feel like we are one *united* team fighting together? Or two *divided* teams fighting against one another?"

The group looked at the opposing side. In that moment, it was clear there was a chasm between them.

"There is a word I want to introduce to you today that was popularized in South Africa." Cooper explained. "That word is *ubuntu.* Ubuntu simply means 'I am because of you' or 'We are because of us.'

Ubuntu is not just a word or an idea—it is a way of living. Ubuntu reminds us of the hard truth. That, when it comes to a team, you are *nothing* without your teammates.

If the offensive line doesn't execute in the trenches, our quarterback doesn't have time to throw the football.

If just one defensive back doesn't get to his landmark in zone coverage, the entire defense gives up an easy touchdown.

If our scout team doesn't push us to the limits in practice, we will be underprepared and exposed on Friday nights," Cooper explained with a fiery passion.

"The Twin Thieves want to make us work *against* our teammates instead of alongside them. That's because fear creates a need to protect your ego and prove your own worth, instead of contributing to the team's purpose. When you work in silos, nobody wins—except our opponent.

The thing is, you don't have to sacrifice your own individual goals to commit to ubuntu. In fact, ubuntu actually increases the odds of you reaching your goals. In all my years of coaching, I've never seen a player find individual success without the help of his teammates."

Cooper turned to address the offense directly.

"Close your eyes and imagine this. There's a minute left in the state championship game, and we're up by one point. Our opponent has the ball and is driving down the field."

Cooper allowed the moment to come alive in the players' minds.

"Time is ticking down. Everything you've been dreaming of is just one minute away. One stop away. But as offensive players, you're left cheering helplessly on the sidelines. In that moment, your dreams depend on the grit, preparation, and execution of your teammates," he said, pointing to the defense.

"How will you feel? Will you wish you poured more into helping your teammates be better? Or will you *know* that you did everything possible to help them be great?"

Cooper reached down and picked up a bundle of sticks from the ground he had gathered during the tug-of-war competition. He tried to break the bundle of sticks but was unsuccessful.

Looking up at the group, Cooper shared. "Sticks in a bundle like this are nearly impossible to break.

However, a single stick"—Cooper took one branch and easily snapped it between his hands—"is vulnerable. And the same applies to people."

Cooper's message to the group was crystal clear.

"Ubuntu is about connectedness, oneness, and togetherness in the face of adversity. If we truly live out ubuntu, we will be unbreakable."

Cooper stepped aside and let Coach Frost share a few reflections on their workout. As he finished, Coach Frost was surprised to see Kade make his way to the middle to break down the team.

"Good work today. But we got a long way to go. Like Coop said, we all gotta work on being better teammates. The enemy isn't in here—it's out there. *I am because you are.* Now let's hear 'ubuntu' on three." The boys huddled around him.

"One-two-three, UBUNTU!"

CHAPTER 14

GOING TO THE EDGE

THE NEXT TUESDAY, Cooper wandered his way around the weight room. To most people, he looked lost, walking aimlessly through the clusters of players. But for Cooper, this was an intentional time to check in on the team. He even had a name for it: *leadership by wandering.*

Most days, he really enjoyed the process. But today, he noticed multiple issues.

In the corner of the weight room, Easton and Sebastian were partnered on the squat rack for what seemed like an hour, going through the motions, talking about everything but the actual workout.

Kade was working hard, yes, but he never spoke up to encourage or coach his younger teammates right next to him.

Above the music, Sebastian's yell broke Cooper's trance.

"Let's gooo!"

His voice echoed through the weight room as he celebrated himself for finishing the last rep on his squat. Sebastian looked toward the coaches to see if they noticed. It was a usual tactic of his—he thought that by being loud, people might think he was working harder than he was.

It didn't fool Cooper. He could tell the young man still hadn't broken a sweat. It was the last straw.

Cooper moved to where Kade was lifting. "Sebastian, Easton! C'mon over here."

As they gathered, Cooper got right to the point.

"You can't just go through the motions if you want to grow. It's not enough. You have to go to the *edge*."

He picked up a pair of five-pound dumbbells and handed them to Sebastian. "Here, Seb, start curling these. How long do you think you could go?"

Sebastian was surprised by the request. He started curling the very light dumbbells. A smile broke across his face.

"I could do this all day!" he responded. Kade and Easton laughed looking on.

"Easy, right?" Cooper responded. "Now put those down and do the same with these."

Cooper handed him the forty-pound dumbbells. Again, Sebastian started curling them. His smile slowly changed into a look of focus.

Cooper pushed him. "C'mon. You can do it. Give me eight more reps."

Finally, after reaching the target, Sebastian let the weights down. Cooper let him catch his breath.

"Now, where would you rather be uncomfortable: here in training or under the bright lights on Friday nights?" Cooper asked.

"Here, I guess." Sebastian responded.

"Exactly," Cooper said in agreement. "Going to the edge means embracing discomfort now, so you aren't exposed when the pressure's on. The edge is where your comfort zone ends and new learning begins.

Think about it this way. When you use the five-pound weights, you feel comfortable, but it's not going to make your muscles grow any bigger.

When you use the forty-pound weights, you're uncomfortable—but you're certainly going to make your muscles grow.

As humans, we're the same way. The problem is, most people continue to pick up the five-pound weights because they want to stay in their comfort zone. Not us. We *live* outside our comfort zone. We take things to the *edge*.

And I want to be very clear. The edge isn't just the last physical reps you do in the weight room.

The edge is any moment of vulnerability where you come toe to toe with the Twin Thieves."

Turning toward Kade, Cooper continued. "For you, curling the forty-pound weights is the easy part. Truly going to the edge, in your case, is speaking up in front of the team, having tough conversations, and pushing your teammates past their comfort zones.

Going to the edge forces you to make a decision. You decide either to retreat in fear, back to your comfort zone—or advance in courage, pushing forward to places you haven't been.

If you want to impress people or look good, the edge isn't the place for you. But if you're looking to grow? It's exactly where you need to be.

I can guarantee you that the pain of going to the edge now is nothing compared to the pain of regret you'll have later for cutting corners.

Every team wants an edge on their opponent. But very few teams are actually willing to consistently go to the edge and *earn it*."

Cooper paused. "Any idea why?" The boys shrugged their shoulders.

"The edge requires work that is hard and excruciatingly painful at times. And going to the edge of your capabilities often isn't pretty. I mean, did you see Sebastian's face on his last reps?"

The boys broke up in smiles, picturing Sebastian grunt out his last reps.

"But the most challenging thing about going to the edge is knowing that you'll face the Twin Thieves there.

We want to build a culture that makes doing the dirty, hard work of going to the edge the cool thing to do. Many people say they want their teammates to go to the edge, but then they are the same ones making fun of them, judging them when they fail, and not going to the edge themselves.

When you go to the edge as the leader, you subconsciously give your teammates permission to take the same risk."

CHAPTER 15

THE LEADERSHIP BLUEPRINT

COOPER COULD TELL that he needed to reinforce his message about going to the edge, specifically for Kade.

Like clockwork the next morning, Kade arrived at 5:30 a.m., early as usual. And all by himself, as usual.

After he changed, Kade walked over to the weight room. He tried opening the door. No luck. Thinking it was stuck, Kade pulled harder to no avail. He didn't realize he was locked out until Cooper's smiling face appeared on the other side of the window.

"Morning, Kade!" Cooper said, voice muffled through the window. "It's great to see you today. But there seems to be a problem." Cooper acted like he was looking for someone behind Kade. "You are all alone. In order for you to get into this weight room, you have to bring at least one of your teammates along with you."

Cooper could see Kade's frustration as he started to understand Cooper's stunt. "Coach, this is ridiculous," Kade said. "I know what you're trying to do. I'm just not that type of leader. I'm the type of leader that leads by example."

Cooper had heard that one a million times. He opened the door and directed Kade into Coach Frost's office. "Come sit down with me. I want to show you something."

As they got into the office, Cooper walked over to the whiteboard, where he'd drawn a three-level triangle. "This is what I call the Leadership Blueprint. As a leader, your mission is to reach the top of this triangle."

Cooper pointed to the bottom level, labeled "Leading Yourself."

"Everything starts with leading yourself. Nobody follows a hypocrite. Leading yourself means having the focus, intensity, and discipline to do the dirty, hard work in the dark. Kade, you are incredible at this level.

But leading yourself just isn't enough to be considered a leader in our culture anymore. In our culture, leading yourself is the *standard.*"

Cooper paused and pointed at the second level, which read "Leading Others."

"Leadership really begins here—when you can lead yourself *and* take the responsibility of leading others."

"But I hate telling people what to do," Kade interjected.

"I get that," Cooper replied. "But what are you really afraid of when it comes to speaking up?"

Kade took a breath, thinking about the question. "I guess I don't want the guys to think that I'm a know-it-all or that I'm better than them."

"Nice!" Cooper's eyes glistened. "The Twin Thieves, specifically the fear of judgment, makes the jump from Leading Yourself to Leading Others the toughest.

But think about it—regardless of what your teammates might think, do you believe that you are better than them?"

"No! Definitely not!" Kade responded.

"Exactly," Cooper replied. "You are coming from a heart posture of care and truly doing it to help them. Now, whether they understand that isn't within your control."

Cooper darkened the line separating levels one and two. "This point—the edge between Leading Yourself and Leading Others—is often the biggest roadblock.

"Leading yourself is relatively safe. You can do your own thing and not ruffle any feathers. But using your voice to lead your teammates, encourage their growth, and hold them accountable? That takes guts.

Because it means telling people what they *need* to hear—which is not always what they *want* to hear. It means figuring out a way to tell the truth with love and empathy."

Kade understood what Cooper shared. Speaking up always seemed to make him uncomfortable.

"Leading others requires you to have a stronger desire for mission accomplishment rather than personal comfort. It forces you to choose the standards of this culture over being liked all the time. True leadership requires you to be okay being disliked in the short term in order to be respected in the long term.

Kade, we need to hear your voice more. Any time you have something to say but don't speak up because of the Twin Thieves, our team misses an opportunity to get better."

Cooper pointed to the apex of the triangle, which he'd labeled "Serving Others."

"The highest level of leadership is committing to serving others. If you can make the jump to leading others, this level will come naturally for you. It means leading your teammates not for your *own* glory but for the *team's*. It means truly being okay as the guide, instead of needing to be the hero.

People that get to this level embrace the fact that leadership often happens in the dark, long after the bright lights have gone out. They commit to the unnoticed and the uncelebrated work behind the scenes that great leadership requires.

The difference between Leading Others and Serving Others is that the leader who *serves* others is truly operating from a heart posture of love."

Cooper put his arm around Kade. "You are doing a heck of a job. I'm really proud of you, but I'm going to keep pushing you. You're a rock on this team. We need you to lean into every bit of the leadership potential you have.

Now, go get a teammate so you can start pumping some iron."

CHAPTER 16

WINNING HEARTS

COACH FROST SAT in his backyard, taking one last look over his patio on the early May afternoon. With summer workouts just one month away, Coach Frost was excited about the growth that he and his players had made. Now, he had the opportunity to get all of his coaches on the same page with their preseason meeting.

Instead of using the usual school conference room, Coach Frost took Cooper's suggestion to host the meeting at his house, grill up burgers, and serve his coaches who gave so much to the program.

After the group enjoyed their meal, Coach Frost spoke up. "Thank you for being here. I know this is different than how we usually do things. But it represents the shift in our culture that I am committed to making."

Coach Frost pointed to one of the coaches in the back. "I asked Coach Hastings to share a letter from Sebastian that he received last season. I think it has some things we can all learn from."

The group of coaches exchanged looks. They all knew Sebastian as an outgoing spirit and talented receiver. He was a likable, charismatic kid, but he also had the frustrating ability to push all of your buttons.

Coach Hastings stood up and unfolded a piece of lined paper. You could tell he was nervous, with all eyes on him as he began to read.

Dear Coach Hastings,

I first want to apologize for acting like a jerk lately. I've held in my anger at the world and taken it out on you. And that's not fair. Most people don't know this, but I've had some really dark moments for parts of the season. I couldn't get this voice out of my head that tormented me. It kept telling me things like:

You are a disappointment.
This is never going to end.
Nobody will notice if you are gone.

But even on the toughest nights when this voice tried to convince me that life wasn't worth living anymore, there was another voice that kept me going.

And that was yours.

I acted like I didn't care about the "sappy" things you'd talk about at practice. I was the first to make fun of them. But the truth was that I was listening. In fact, I kept a list of my favorite "Hastings Quotes" in my phone to read when I felt most alone:

"A smooth sea never made a skillful sailor."
"Life gives the toughest battles to the strongest warriors."
"Be strong because things will get better. This storm too shall pass."

Thank you for believing in me when I gave you every reason not to. You helped me find the courage to ask for help, and now, I am feeling so much better.

You not only inspired me this season—I truly believe you saved my life.

Love,
Sebastian

Tears welled in his eyes as he read the last sentence and folded up the paper. It was clear the coaches appreciated Coach Hasting's courage to share.

Coach Frost stood up in front of the group. "Cooper Williams asked me a question that I've been thinking about: 'How would you lead your team differently if you knew at least one player was questioning if their life was worth living?'"

Coach Frost paused to let the question sink in. He knew this conversation was more vulnerable than any they had engaged in before.

"And, if I'm being honest, the thing that hurts me the most about Sebastian's story is that I'm around him every day, yet I completely missed it. How many of you had a similar feeling when hearing that?"

Hands shot up around the patio.

"Every day, I hope that you reflect on Sebastian's note. Because he is not alone." Coach Frost slowly shook his head. "We have more than 100 athletes. It's a pretty good chance there's other players who feel the same way, struggling in a really dark place. And our opportunity is to help pull them through the darkness.

Going forward in this program, I am committed to making a massive shift. Don't get me wrong. I still want to win games, win conference titles, and win state championships. But above all of that, our number one priority will be *winning our players' hearts and minds*."

Coach Frost spoke with more conviction than the assistants had ever felt from him before.

"Before our players love the message, we have to get them to love the messenger. And to do that requires a relentless, championship-level commitment in learning about our people. We need to become elite trust builders. If we want to lead them better, we have to read them better.

What we do matters. But *how we do it* matters even more.

Building the trust we need with players requires daily deposits into our relationships. Those small, seemingly insignificant deposits will always come back to pay off in a big way.

And like Coach Hastings has experienced, that payoff is often way bigger than winning football games. You might even save a kid's life."

CHAPTER 17

THE TRUST FRAMEWORK

THE NEXT MORNING, Coach Frost was in his office preparing for the upcoming parent meeting when he heard a knock at the door.

"Morning, Ed! What? Are you already coming to get my burger recipe?" Coach Frost asked jokingly. After they shared a laugh and some small talk on the night before, Ed got down to business.

"Coach, our meeting last night was different than any we've had in all our years together. It was emotional, no doubt. Left me thinking all night."

Ed paused, trying to figure out how to articulate his thoughts.

"I want to be on this journey with you. You know, winning hearts and becoming elite trust builders. But here's the thing. Trust is so vague. It sounds good and all, but what does it really look like? If I'm being honest, I just don't know how to do it. I kinda feel like you're either a great trust builder or you aren't."

Coach Frost listened intently and nodded along.

"I'm glad that you asked that question. In fact, I've been talking a lot about this with Cooper and our Leadership Council," he said, motioning to the whiteboard.

The whiteboard that was usually scribbled with play diagrams now had a single equation on it:

$$\text{TRUST} = \frac{\text{CARE} + \text{CREDIBILITY} + \text{RELIABILITY}}{\text{AUTHENTIC VULNERABILITY}}$$

"Cooper calls this the Trust Framework," Coach Frost told him. "It takes the idea of trust and breaks it down into four concrete fundamental areas that can be developed. It shows that great trust builders don't become that way by accident. They are great because they dominate in these areas."

Coach Frost paused. "I'm still learning all this myself, but I think it will help answer your question."

Ed nodded, staring intently at the whiteboard.

"Building effective trust starts with practicing 'authentic vulnerability.'

Am I secure with who I am?
Do I truly trust myself?
Can I take tough feedback?
Do I know my strengths?

And most importantly: am I aware of the fears, insecurities, and weaknesses that can create blind spots? Because if we don't recognize and own our limitations, they own us."

Coach Frost pointed at the next word in the equation.

"'Care' is how we let the people we lead know they matter more than their performance.

Care is twofold: it's about having both the mindset that everybody matters and the skill set to demonstrate it. *This* is where listening becomes a superpower and rounding becomes essential."

"Rounding?" Ed questioned.

"It's a technique I learned from Cooper. Rounding is when you intentionally go around and have trust-building conversations with everybody you're leading. It's about systematically connecting with your team, making sure nobody is slipping through the cracks.

I'll be the first to admit that, when the stress of the season starts to build, I can go a few days—if not *weeks*—without checking in with certain coaches or players. Cooper's been challenging me and the player leaders to build a checklist, where we report back on who we connected with weekly."

Ed nodded, and Coach Frost pointed to the next fundamental.

"'Credibility' is about being the best, most technically advanced coach possible. This is one we've always preached. Our drills, our feedback, our communication—it all has to be on the cutting edge. Players have to *feel* that you're giving them a unique advantage as their coach."

Coach Frost moved to the last fundamental.

"And the last is 'Reliability.' This is about showing up in the toughest moments again and again. It's about getting better when things get tougher. It's about our players knowing that you won't retreat when the pressure is on."

Coach Frost let the concepts sink in. "One of the challenging things about trust is that it is built over time. It takes months—if not *years*—of showing up every day, walking the talk, and being reliable.

Trust is like climbing a ladder. You can't get to the top in one step, but you can certainly get to the bottom with one misstep."

Coach Frost settled back into his chair.

"Ed, the reality is I've left trust building up to chance for far too long. But we never had a process to talk about this specifically. I want to be as *intentional* about these fundamentals as we are with physical fundamentals.

Each week, we'll be setting aside time to cultivate these skills. And we will be using pulse surveys to truly learn from all our players to see where we are at."

Coach Frost expected Ed's look of surprise.

"I know, I know—our practice time is tight. But there are trade-offs for everything, and I'm no longer okay with overlooking the culture of our team."

Ed nodded along with Coach Frost. He was still a bit uncertain how this would look, but one thing was certain. He had not felt this level of conviction from Coach Frost in all the years they had worked together. And for that one reason alone, he was more excited than ever to start another season.

CHAPTER 18

TRUE ACCOUNTABILITY

IT WAS 5:45 a.m. on a breezy June morning. The first day of summer workouts. As the group of young men converged on the big "A" at the fifty-yard line, a gradual slow clap reverberated around the stadium.

Clap...clap...clap...clap.

The clapping grew faster, ending in a powerful breakdown. You could see the goose bumps popping up on Coach Frost's arms. This was special, and he could feel it. It was clear the players shared Coach Frost's excitement.

"Gentlemen!" Coach Frost yelled out. "Welcome to the next step in our journey."

Dew covered the field, along with oversized tires, sledgehammers, battle ropes, and sandbags. You name it, Coach Frost had it on the turf.

"When our opportunity comes this year, we *will* be ready. A lot of teams like talking about greatness until they have to do the dirty work that greatness requires. Today is about deeds, not words.

Leaders: now is the time to lead. Let's put everything that we've learned from Cooper to work."

Sebastian took advantage of the moment.

"All right, boys, time to bring it!" He turned to the back of the group. "Freshmen, you just try to keep up, okay? Let's go!"

The huddle broke and players hustled to their designated stations. Cooper and Coach Frost had spent the week devising special groups to help mix the seniors with underclassmen. Cooper set off wandering to check on how members of the Leadership Council were doing.

Near the end zone, he saw Easton's group flipping tires. A skinny sophomore was struggling with the massive hunk of rubber.

"Dude, if it's too heavy for you, just leave it. You gotta keep moving," Easton said in a tone more condescending than encouraging.

Over by the away team's bench, Sebastian's voice rang out.

"This isn't youth league anymore—we actually work here! Pick it up, let's go!"

Cooper shook his head. His wandering brought him to the fifty-yard line, where a sweaty freshman struggled pushing the heavy sled. He put his foot behind the kid's heel to provide some stability.

"You got this. Come on! Puushhhh!"

The freshman groaned and put his whole body into it. The sled finally glided past the fifteen-yard line. He bent over, hands on knees, but smiling from ear to ear.

"Coach, can we get a five-minute water break?" Cooper called out. "I wanna chat with the Leadership Council over here."

The nine young men gathered around Cooper.

"How do you all think things are going?" he asked the group.

"I think we're doing a good job," Easton offered. "Calling out the young guys when they aren't meeting our standards."

Sebastian echoed his QB. "Yeah, I mean I got some *real* clueless freshmen over there, but we're being vocal like you asked. We're holding them accountable."

"Being a vocal leader and holding your teammates accountable is more than just yelling at people and pointing out their mistakes," Cooper said. "It's about calling people *up*, not calling them *out*. As a leader, you can be demanding without being demeaning.

When you use the word 'accountability,' you're often just giving yourself the illusion of control. The truth is, you can't control other people's actions. But you *can* use your influence to guide them."

Kade took a break from chugging his water to speak up.

"I get what you're saying. But then how do we respond when they're not doing what they're supposed to do?" he asked Cooper.

"It starts with you being the hardest worker in the group. How does it feel to be held accountable by somebody that is slacking themselves?"

Easton chuckled and chimed in. "Honestly, it makes me want to give them the finger much more than listen to them."

"Exactly," Cooper responded with a smile. "And why would any of your teammates be different than you? You have no credibility telling people what to do if you're slacking yourself.

So first exemplify the standard. Then roll up your sleeves and work alongside your teammates. Guide them, encourage them, push them to levels they didn't think they could reach. Believe in them more than they even believe in *themselves*.

Your influence as a leader depends on the trust you've built with them through your words and actions in the past. Show them what it means to care about your teammates. Become a model of the high standards we have. Then pull those teammates up to the new standard we've created.

Constantly calling out your teammates is easy and may produce some immediate, superficial results. But fear and shame burn out fast. Influencing people over the long term is hard and requires hours of work behind the scenes.

It's easy to yell at somebody and then just turn your back.
It's hard to guide them, encourage them, and continue showing up until they succeed.

It's easy to point somebody out for being late.
It's hard to get up early, show up at their doorstep, and give them a ride.

It's easy to yell at a teammate for missing a line while running.
It's hard to do another rep and run alongside them so they meet the standard.

It's easy to call people out.
It's way harder to call them up.

The mission of great leadership is to increase your level of care and empathy *without* lowering the standard."

Cooper paused to scan the group. "One of the most powerful things a leader can say in a culture is, 'That's not how we do things here.' And the true impact of those words depends on the influence you've developed prior to that moment."

Cooper paused, ready to send the players back out on the field.

"And one other thing," Cooper said. "Don't just pick out the youngest, weakest link to challenge, support, and guide. Some of you seem very comfortable calling out the freshman, but you didn't even say a word to your senior buddy who was slacking right next to you.

True accountability requires you to have the courage to confront teammates who are also your friends. They may not understand at the time, but that's okay."

Coach Frost blew his whistle to signal the end of the break.

"Remember: You can plant the seeds of change, but you can't force the seed to grow. Let Coach Frost be the enforcer if need be—you all focus on being influencers.

The greatest leaders have the unique ability to move the human heart while continuing to have extremely high standards.

Growing a great culture requires a movement, not a mandate. Now let's get back to work."

CHAPTER 19

INTO THE STORM

THE NEXT DAY, Kade and Trey approached Cooper before their workout. Cooper could tell they had something on their mind.

"Cooper." Kade started the conversation. "Could we talk to you for a second?"

"Sure. What's going on?"

"Trey and I were talking about our conversation on accountability yesterday and..." Kade hesitated, and his eyes went down to his shoes before going on. "Well, we think Ryan is making choices on the weekend that aren't living out our team standards."

Cooper listened intently. "I see." He responded slowly. "So have you talked to him about it?"

"Well, kinda," Kade responded. "We've tried to let him know that he needs to do things differently."

"Kinda, huh?" Cooper smiled. "Well, it sounds like this is an opportunity for the both of you to have a tough conversation. But you both have to decide: Will you have the mindset of a cow? Or a buffalo?"

The boys looked at Cooper, a bit confused by the reference.

Cooper went on: "Let me explain. On the plains of Colorado, something interesting happens to the wildlife when storm clouds roll through.

When the cows sense a storm approaching, they hightail it in the opposite direction, trying to escape it. But cows can't outrun a storm. Eventually, it catches them—and they end up right in the thick of it, suffering as they're forced to put up with the treacherous conditions. By continuing to run and avoid the storm, the cows actually end up *in the storm* for much longer.

Herds of buffalo respond differently. When buffalo sense a storm coming, they move straight into the dark, windy skies. By heading *into* the storm, they spend less time in danger and come out on the other side with fewer injuries.

Now back to your situation. So far, have you approached this conversation with Ryan head-on and directly like a buffalo? Or tried to avoid it like a cow?"

Kade and Trey cringed, knowing clearly what the answer was. "Probably more like a cow."

Cooper smiled. "And that is why this is an awesome opportunity for you to practice putting this on top of the table and delivering the mail to the right address."

The boys looked at Cooper for more explanation.

"Instead of confronting Ryan directly, most people would avoid the direct, honest conversation and spread the mail to the wrong address. They go to everybody else except Ryan to try and solve the issue."

The boys both exhaled. They knew what had to be done but were just apprehensive about what could play out.

"But let's be real," Cooper continued. "What is really holding you back from having this conversation?"

Trey spoke up for the first time. "Honestly, Coach, I'm worried because Ryan has been my friend for a long time, and I just don't know how he'll take it."

Cooper smiled.

"Worrying is like a rocking chair—it gives you something to do, but it doesn't get you anywhere. You can worry all you want, but without action, you are in the same spot.

The Twin Thieves are always stronger when you are *not* working on the problem. Productive action helps alleviate anxiety.

It's not the tough conversation that is the toughest storm you need to go headfirst into. It's the Twin Thieves gripping you, trying to make you fearful and avoid the conversation.

Many people think courage is reserved for superheroes wearing capes. But it isn't. Extraordinary courage is found in ordinary people consistently choosing to go into the storm, day after day.

We need you to shift your mindset from a cow to a buffalo by reframing how you see the situation. Running from the storms to seek immediate comfort will only prolong the pain."

Cooper put his arm around Trey.

"Courage isn't about being fearless—it's about feeling the fear, the uncertainty, the nerves and *doing it anyway*.

Fearless doesn't mean you have less fear, it just means you choose to make decisions that are less based on your fears.[6]

Inside of a culture, both fear and courage are contagious. The one that spreads the most depends on the daily decisions of leaders like you."

Cooper started walking alongside the boys. "Don't run from this storm. Go toward it. It is within these storms that your greatness can emerge."

---

6 David Nurse quote

CHAPTER 20

WATER THE BAMBOO

THE LINCOLN VALLEY Passing Tournament was a checkpoint every year for how the Aviators were progressing. Landing on the last weekend of June, it was a gathering of some of the state's best teams. Most years, Coach Frost and the players left feeling good about themselves. But after a subpar performance, this year felt more deflating than exciting.

In particular, Cooper could tell Trey looked frustrated. When he asked him what was up, Trey didn't hold back.

"Why is it so much harder for me as a leader? When I was a freshman, the senior leaders like DJ or Turner didn't have any issues like this!"

Cooper listened with deep care and empathy. The rest of the team was close enough to overhear, so he let them gather around.

"Can you all connect with how he's feeling?" Cooper asked the group.

After affirming nods, he shared with a smile, "Has anyone ever told you the story of bamboo?"

The players shook their heads.

Cooper shared, "You see, many people love bamboo. They love the bamboo trees, and they love the bamboo wood—but very few people understand the arduous process of growing bamboo. First, you dig up the soil and make sure it is fertile, and then you plant the bamboo seed. Then you must faithfully water it every day. After three months, guess what starts to happen?"

"The bamboo tree starts to sprout up out of the ground?" Trey responded, still in a state of frustration.

"Nothing! You see absolutely nothing happening. For an entire year, you can water it and water it—and you still won't see any progress. Do you know what happens after two years?"

Trey replied, more tentatively this time, "It starts to sprout up out of the ground?"

"Nothing! You still see absolutely nothing," Cooper explained.

"That's because the development is all happening *beneath the surface.*

Beneath the surface, a massive, dense foundation of roots is spreading out all throughout the ground to prepare for the rapid growth that the bamboo will experience. So, you keep watering it and watering it, and eventually, after three years of seeing nothing at all happen above the surface—the bamboo tree shoots up to over ninety feet tall in just six weeks!

Most people want the ninety-foot-tall bamboo tree without the years of root development. But without the years of invisible growth, the bamboo wouldn't have a solid foundation, and it could never sustain the massive and rapid growth that occurs." Cooper paused to let the lesson sink in.

"I know this tournament was tough. But the question is: *will you all continue to water the bamboo?*

Like the roots of a bamboo tree, building a championship culture is a long process of invisible growth, where you are building the foundation that is necessary to sustain success.

Our society is addicted to instant gratification. We want things right away—but success isn't microwavable. Things that matter—relationships, character, leadership—don't grow overnight. They take years of watering.

And there will be many distractions along the way. There will be people who tell you that you are stupid or crazy for working so hard. There will be people who try and lure you off the path with quick fixes and get-rich-quick schemes. But you must be wise, stay the path, and continue to build your foundation together.

You see, it's the periods of invisible growth when the Twin Thieves are most alive. When nothing seems to be getting better, that's when the fear of failure and judgment kicks in, telling you lies like:

You are wasting your time!
You are an embarrassment.
You are a disappointment.

But these moments of doubt are conquerable when you have the strength and confidence of your teammates behind you.

Don't believe the myths. Leadership isn't sexy—it's frustrating, it's mundane, and it requires a ridiculous amount of work in the dark. But it's a whole lot easier when you have great teammates on the journey with you.

This team has a bright future ahead of it if you can stay the path.

Just never forget to water the bamboo."

CHAPTER 21

DON'T SINK THE SHIP

THE WHISTLE BLEW, and everyone took a knee around Coach Frost. The July heat radiated from the turf. The Aviators were allowed five football-specific practices over the duration of their summer training. Coach Frost was determined to use every bit of them.

"We get limited opportunities to put on the pads during the summer, so let's take advantage of every chance to get better! Leaders, this is your ship. Who wants to break us down?"

Kade jumped into the middle of the circle.

"Let's go, guys! Invest in every rep! It's like putting money in your piggy bank. Every rep, every snap, every opportunity is like making a deposit. Whoever has the biggest piggy bank when the season rolls around will be able to cash in. Let's fill those piggy banks today!"

The whistle blew again, and everyone sprinted to their position coaches.

Cooper walked by the offensive linemen and noticed Kade talking to a sophomore who didn't finish his sprint completely through the line. He could hear Kade from twenty feet away.

"That's not how we do things around here, Mason. In our program, we always finish three yards past the line. Those little things are what separate us from everyone else. Focus on finishing."

Kade gave the sophomore a reassuring smile and a fist bump and hopped back into line. Cooper smiled.

On the other side of the field, Coach Frost was watching Trey work with a young linebacker on some basic footwork drills.

He also noticed Sebastian was spending his water break talking with some of the young wide receivers instead of hanging out with Easton. He was impressed.

After the practice wrapped up, Cooper asked to meet with the Leadership Council.

Cooper had the large whiteboard the offensive line coach used to draw up blocking schemes, but there weren't any plays drawn on the board today. Instead, there was a poorly drawn sailboat floating on top of some water.

"Who drew that, one of Coach Frost's daughters?" Sebastian asked with a chuckle.

The players started laughing.

"Nope! This is the best I could do, Sebastian," Cooper said, smiling. "What I attempted to draw here is a ship in the ocean. I wanted to provide a visual for you all." He turned and pointed at the drawing.

"Ships are pretty incredible things. They can weigh up to 60,000 tons and *still* manage to float. Ultimately, it is not the water *around* a ship that sinks it—it sinks when water gets *inside*. You are starting to build a strong ship. Coach Frost and I could see that today.

I saw Trey helping a young linebacker during the break. Sebastian was intentionally connecting with the younger receivers. Kade was being vocal and practicing true accountability."

Coach Frost stood in the back, smiling like a proud father.

Cooper stepped closer toward the group of players taking a knee. "As you continue to build this culture, you must understand that it's not the things outside of this program that will ruin it—it's when you allow the wrong things *inside*. It's not our opponent or the media that will sink this ship. It's us.

My question for you all: what could potentially sink this culture if we allow it in our ship?"

Cooper paused to let the players think.

"Think about teams you have been a part of in the past. What held those teams back from becoming the best versions of themselves?"

The members of the Leadership Council were getting more and more comfortable speaking up. As the responses came in quickly, Cooper wrote the words inside the picture of the ship on the whiteboard.

Entitlement
Complacency
Drama
Selfish players
Social media
Judgment
Cliques on the team
Gossip…not delivering mail to the right address
Ego
Poor decision making off the field
Negative attitudes
Not taking care of the "little things"
Jealousy

"Excellent," Cooper said as he finished writing everything inside the ship. "And all of those are rooted in the Twin Thieves.

In any team, school, or organization, most of these things happen when the head coach, the principal, or the president of the company isn't around.

Most of the things that sink the ship happen after meetings, in the locker room, on the weekends, or on your cell phones when there are no coaches present.

As leaders, it is *your* job to make sure these things do not enter our ship. And the first step is being aware of what we need to keep out.

The collective impact you have on your teammates is extremely powerful. This peer pressure can push a culture to the next level—or it can sink a culture entirely. The choice is yours.

If you can put on blinders to eliminate the outside noise and focus on taking care of your ship—this group can go *far.*

And let me tell ya—it will be one hell of a ride!"

CHAPTER 22

PURPOSE > PAIN

"Up! Down! Up! Down!"

As everybody's legs turned to jelly, David, the US Navy SEAL facilitating the camp, blew his whistle.

"Everybody bring it in! Good work." He walked to the front of the group.

Visiting Camp McCoy was a new experience for the team. Cooper had known David for a long time. He knew David had a masterful ability to use the exact amount of physical training to help people tap into their greatest mental strength.

With official practice just one week away, the training with David was a great way to test the strength of the Aviators' growing culture.

"Right now, you could be in so many different places, doing things that are much easier than this. Things that are more enjoyable. Why did you make the effort to come? What is your purpose? *Why are you here?*"

David let the question linger under the hot sun.

"I've heard you guys have big dreams. The thing about big dreams is they require incredible amounts of sacrifice, commitment, and struggle. Most people can't endure the pain required to achieve big dreams. But people with a powerful purpose can.

Purpose inspires toughness.

When you look behind the story of people who endured uncommon amounts of pain to reach their dreams, they were often fueled by a powerful purpose. This purpose was their North Star—guiding them, motivating them, and pulling them forward.

Kyle Maynard climbed 19,431 feet to the top of Mount Kilimanjaro. And he did it without arms or legs. His purpose amid the pain was to honor fallen veterans, one of which he promised to deliver his ashes to the summit.

Charlotte Heffelmire was nineteen when she found her dad on the brink of death, pinned beneath a truck. She lifted the 7,000-pound truck by herself, allowing him to escape. Her purpose was saving her father's life.

Viktor Frankl witnessed some of the worst pain and suffering in human history inside of Nazi concentration camps. Afterward, he said that the people most likely to survive were those with the strongest purpose.

Many people blame pain when they give up on their dreams. But the pain isn't to blame. It's their lack of purpose.

Society tries to trick us into believing that fulfillment comes from avoiding pain and sacrifice. But the truth is that your highest levels of grit, growth, and fulfillment often come *after* the most painful struggle, hardship, and sacrifice.

So: what is your purpose—what is your *why* for doing all this? Think about it. Reflect on it. Once you get clarity around your why, I want you to write it on your cleats. And I challenge you to choose a purpose that can't be taken away from you based on what a scoreboard says.

And on the toughest, most painful days when you don't feel like lacing up your cleats for practice, read what you wrote. It'll remind you that you don't need to escape the pain. You can use the pain to transform into a better version of yourself."

David blew the whistle sharply.

"All right, speech over. Back on your feet!"

CHAPTER 23

STORY TIME

AFTER A DAY of intense workouts, the team showered, ate dinner, and prepared to relax at a campfire that David invited them to. Their bodies ached, but they were excited to get the opportunity to hang with their teammates and a Navy SEAL. As they filtered into the clearing, the players took a seat on half logs that circled the fire pit.

After welcoming everybody, David kicked things off.

"When people hear that I'm a Navy SEAL, they have a lot of questions. And one of the most popular ones is: at what point was I willing to die for the SEAL next to me?"

The group of boys locked in on David. It wasn't hard to get teenagers to listen to a Navy SEAL, but Cooper could tell they were especially captured by the vulnerability of this tough soldier.

"For me, that moment came when I started learning about the person behind the uniform. When I got to know the human behind the SEAL. I learned that—although we were very different—in so many ways, we were the same.

All of us loved our country. We had similar hopes. Similar dreams. And we had similar fears.

The more that I learned about the person next to me, the more impossible it was *not* to give them everything I had. Even if that meant my own life.

Their purpose became part of my purpose.

Tonight, I'm challenging you all to learn about your teammates through a vulnerable conversation: What is the toughest challenge that you've faced in your life? And how have you grown because of it?"

The stillness among the group matched the weight of the questions. David watched them contemplate their answer, waiting patiently for the first person to share.

Slowly, Coach Frost stood up.

"When I was eight years old, my dad was going through a rough time. He turned to alcohol. I can still remember...hearing him come home after the bar closed. The shivers and fear that ran through my body. It was paralyzing.

It got to a point where it was happening nightly, and I quickly learned that my only refuge was hiding in the coat closet, praying that he wouldn't find me."

The players listened intently. They had never heard this part of Coach Frost's story before. They'd barely even considered his life before coaching.

"There were nights when I would hear his footsteps come by so close that I'd hold my breath like I was underwater. Not making a sound. Most nights, he would just walk by, and I would let out a huge exhale, knowing I was safe. But there were nights when he'd open that closet and find me waiting with nowhere to escape."

Coach Frost stopped for a moment, replaying those memories in his mind. His eyes glistened off the fire as he looked around at the group.

"Those were painful, painful times. And it went on for a couple of years before my mother finally left. There's still things that I'm working through from those days to process and understand.

But when I look back, I guess I learned that if *that* couldn't stop me, I don't know what could. And eventually, I went into coaching because I know some of you are in similar positions. And I want you to know that you are never alone. I'm here for you."

When Coach stopped, a few kids in the group started slowly clapping and the rest joined in. After a few moments of silence, Trey stood up.

"I've known many of you all for a long time, but only a few know what I'm about to share."

There was a wavering in Trey's voice. He looked down at his shoes. This was miles away from his comfort zone.

"My dad left our family when I was eleven. My brother was two, and my sister was only six months. My mom did her best to take care of us, but it didn't last long."

Trey stopped and started to tear up as he shared. His teammates were glued to his every word.

"A year ago, my mom was arrested in front of us for getting caught up in the wrong stuff. We haven't seen her since. Imagine explaining that to your five-year-old brother.

For a while, the state system told me that my siblings and I would have to be separated. Luckily, my grandma took us in. To this day, my siblings and I live with her. The challenge is she is getting older and weaker, so I've kinda become the main caretaker in the house."

Wiping away the tears, Trey continued.

"I ain't asking for sympathy. But some things are just really tough. Especially mornings. I know I've been late multiple times for morning workouts. But I just want you guys to know that it's not because I don't care.

Every morning, my alarm goes off at 4:30 a.m. to pack lunches. To do laundry. To get breakfast. And to get my brother and sister on the bus.

Sometimes things just take longer, and then I feel embarrassed for showing up late."

It was clear this had been weighing on Trey for a while. He took a deep breath.

"And the truth is I'm still in the middle of this. So I'm not exactly sure what I've learned yet. But I just felt like sharing this with you all."

Trey sat back down and the group broke into applause. And nobody clapped more genuinely than Sebastian. He felt sick to his stomach thinking about the passive-aggressive comments he'd made to Trey for being late over the years. He had no idea what his teammate was going through.

As the night went on, coaches and players alike shared real, vulnerable moments that they had lived through.

Once they finished, David stood back up front.

"You know, a lot of people view vulnerability as a weakness. But inside of a trusting group like this, being open and willing to share is the furthest thing from weakness. It's a *strength*.

The Twin Thieves are quick to cast judgment toward your teammates.

They are just lazy.
They just don't care.
They're selfish.
They're a jerk.

Don't believe the immediate assumptions.

Get curious before furious.

Just like I made it a priority to learn about the person behind the SEAL, you must learn about the person behind the player.

If you make your teammate's purpose part of your purpose, I guarantee you will unlock levels of commitment, strength, and grit within yourself that you didn't even know existed."

CHAPTER 24

THE LITTLE THINGS

THE START OF August meant the first official practice of the season had finally arrived. It was like Christmas Day for Coach Frost, and the players were just as excited as he was.

As the team got into their drills, their renewed energy was a breath of fresh air. But it was careless, erratic, and unfocused. Cooper asked Coach Frost to slow things down. He blew his whistle and brought the group together.

Cooper shared, "Everybody in the state is starting practice today. Everybody will break down film. Everybody will have meetings.

So what will make us any different than everybody else?"

Cooper paused to scan the group. "This team may be more connected than ever, but we need to use that connection to push each other to do the gritty, dirty hard work.

Connection is important, but it isn't the only ingredient to being the best you can be."

The players nodded along to Cooper's words.

"It's not just *what* we do—it's also *how* we do it that will shape our culture, drive our results, and ultimately, separate us from everybody else." Cooper continued with passion.

"How we practice.
How we communicate.
How we finish through the drill.
How we respond to adversity.

How we listen.
How we lead.
How we serve.
And as simple as how we carry the ball.

So how do *we* practice? We practice with an intense focus on the details. We practice with maximal intent. We want to be the very best at the basics. It isn't sexy, but the very best in the world are the best at the basics.

Kobe Bryant once said, 'Why do you think I'm the best player in the world? Because I never ever get bored with the basics.'

A lot of times, when teams get beat, their first instinct is to say: 'We need to get back to the basics.'

This year, we are not going to have to go back to the basics—because we are never going to leave them in the first place."

The entire group was locked in, absorbing Cooper's competitive fire.

Cooper continued. "The better you get, the person most likely to beat you is *you*! Complacency is contagious, and it can fool you into overlooking the fundamentals.

This sounds simple—but remaining intensely focused on the little things *consistently* is extremely difficult.

There will be some days you don't feel like it. But in our culture, our standards will always trump our feelings. And the standard in this program is your absolute *best*.

This year, our goal isn't to win with the flashy plays. Our goal is to grind other teams down with the relentless execution of the little things."

The team got back to work with a laser focus on the details, but Coach Frost and Cooper knew this wasn't going to be the last time they needed to refocus the group.

As practice wrapped up, there was one more thing that needed to be discussed: the selection of team captains. Coach Frost had always picked the captains, but this year he wanted the team to make the decision. He gathered them all on the turf.

"I appreciate how you were able to refocus from the start of practice. The ability to refocus is an essential skill. It's the mark of a mature team. I'd like all of the members of our Leadership Council to come to the front of the group."

The six members got up and walked to the front.

"On your way out of practice today," Coach Frost continued, "I want you to vote for one player on offense and one player on defense that is currently standing up here.

Now, before you make your pick, I want to stress that this is not a popularity contest. This is an opportunity for you all to recognize two teammates that you feel live out our values every day. Players that you think embody the mindset we're trying to build here.

Great leaders don't allow their circumstances to dictate their behavior. When you make your selection, consider the leaders on this team that are consistent in their words and their actions. Consider the ones who do the dirty work and lead in the dark," Coach Frost said passionately.

After the team breakdown, Cooper asked the Leadership Council to stick around.

"Listen, Coach Frost and I went back and forth about having captains and the purpose of captains. Regardless of the outcome, the key is how each of you responds.

For this team to grow, we need each of you to grow as leaders, too. We need each of you to drive this culture in a positive direction, even if you don't have the captain patch on your jersey," Cooper said with authority.

STEVE JONES + LUCAS JADIN

As the Leadership Council dispersed, Coach Frost approached Cooper.

"Well, Coop—looks like Trey and Kade got the most votes," Coach Frost said. "Kade's gonna be the first junior captain we've ever had."

Cooper smiled. He'd witnessed firsthand Kade's dedication over the summer, and he felt like a proud dad seeing it start to pay off.

"It'll be interesting to see how Easton and his dad handle this one," Coach Frost said, laughing nervously.

"You know, Coach, you can always use the trump card and make Easton the captain."

Coach Frost looked over at the boys leaving the field and thought for a minute.

"That'd definitely make things easier for me, Coop. But that's not what's best for this team. The players have spoken, and it's up to me to follow their lead. Kade and Trey are our captains."

CHAPTER 25

UNCONDITIONAL LOVE

Sitting in his office that Friday morning, Coach Frost couldn't stop fidgeting. He was nervous. That night, the Aviators would take the field for the first time of the season. And their coach would finally see if all their work had made a difference.

Game days always seemed to drag on for Coach Frost. The anticipation, the anxiety, the uncertainty—it slowed time to a standstill. He wanted to fast-forward to being under those beautiful Friday night lights.

Six hours before kickoff, his phone started vibrating on his desk. He picked it up and saw a text from Cooper.

Hey, Coach. Don't forget to tell your players you love them.

Love? Coach Frost sighed.

Despite Cooper's continuous use of the word, it still made Coach Frost uncomfortable. As a player, he'd never heard his coaches say it. And as a coach, it hadn't even been in his vocabulary.

But he'd been to Cooper's house—he'd seen the results of a leader who embraced love. It created players who *wanted* to succeed for their coach. It created coaches who felt invested in their players' success.

Cooper had planted a seed with his text message. And as the day went on, Coach Frost continued to think about the text and the word *love*. The more he thought about it, the more he knew Cooper was right.

These kids were his pride and joy. They were respectful. They worked hard—heck, during the season, Coach Frost spent more time with them than he did his own family.

I guess I do love these kids, he thought.

The thought continued to bounce around his head as he left his office for the team's pregame meal. He got to the cafeteria and surveyed the pack of hungry young men. Coach Frost could feel their nervous tension. They were just as anxious as he was.

He stepped up in front and asked for everyone's attention.

"Gentlemen, I can tell you're nervous. That's good. I would be worried if you weren't nervous. That means you care—not just about winning, but *about each other.*

This summer, David asked you to write your 'why' on your football cleats. That's because people with a strong why are resilient. Teams with a strong why are *unstoppable.*

This year, we're going to start a new tradition. Each week, before we eat our pregame meal, I am going to ask a couple of you to share your why with the entire team. This week, I'll start."

Coach Frost paused and gathered his courage.

"I'll be honest. My why had always been winning football games. Winning a state championship. Becoming a dynasty. And don't get me wrong—I still want those things," Coach Frost said, grinning.

"But now, my why—my *purpose* in leading this program—has changed. This off-season, I realized something important. I'm not a football coach. I'm a leader who happens to coach football.

And my purpose as a leader is to help each one of you reach your full potential.

Ultimately, my why is *you*."

All eyes were locked on him.

"I love you guys."

The room grew silent. Nobody expected those words to come out of Coach's mouth.

"And that love is unconditional."

He paused and took a breath. He'd said the words, but still some of the players looked confused as to what he meant by it.

"When I say 'unconditional love,' that means I love each of you for *who you are*—not for what you do.

It is easy to feel like your value as a person is greater when you play more downs, or score more touchdowns, or get more tackles. The truth is that your value is constant. It is priceless, and it doesn't go up or down based on results or your performance. Every human being is infinitely valuable."

Coach Frost could feel the invisible weight being lifted off the players' shoulders as they seemed to collectively exhale. It was powerful.

"No matter what happens on that field tonight, know that you are loved."

The speech was all they needed to be fully riled up for the game. And as Coach Frost wrapped up, the cafeteria started buzzing again. It was time to play some football.

After they'd all eaten, the Leadership Council stayed behind to help pick up the cafeteria. As they walked out, Trey stopped suddenly and turned to Coach Frost.

"Coach? You know, that was the first time I've ever heard an adult male tell me that he loved me." Trey avoided eye contact as tears welled up in his eyes.

"Thank you for giving me that today."

Coach Frost pulled him in for a hug, and Trey embraced it.

"Coach...I love you too."

CHAPTER 26

CATCHING CHAMPIONS

Four weeks of the football season had passed, and the Aviators had spent it getting win after win after win. They'd come out roaring in the first half of the season, going 4-0 and looking downright unstoppable.

In their most recent contest, Easton had notched over 200 yards and four touchdowns—two of them on deep balls to Sebastian. Trey tore the opposing offense to shreds, racking up fourteen tackles and two sacks. The defense didn't give up a single point. They were on top of the world.

It was tradition for the team to meet on Sunday nights to focus on the game plan for their upcoming opponent. This year, though, Cooper and Coach Frost decided to implement a meeting with the Leadership Council just before. Since the Leadership Council was meant to serve as a bridge between the coaching staff and players, these weekly meetings helped Coach Frost get a pulse on the team.

"Great to see you all," Cooper said as they rolled into the room. The leaders were all smiles, still riding high off the Friday night blowout. "How is our ship doing?"

Cooper always tried to let the players talk the majority of the meeting, even if it meant sitting in uncomfortable silence while the players gathered their thoughts.

Easton finally spoke up. "We're doing great, Cooper. I think our passing game was on point last Friday night. Sebastian and I are really feeling it right now."

Sebastian nodded his head in agreement with Easton. "Yeah, we need to keep throwing the ball down the field. Nobody can keep up with us!"

The Leadership Council went around, and each one shared their thoughts about their performance on the field. It wasn't exactly what Cooper was looking for.

"Those were some highlights," Cooper said, pushing them. "But what about our ship?

Is there anything getting into our ship that we can't have?
How are we combating the Twin Thieves?
Are we living out our values? Or are they just words on a poster?
How is our leadership in the dark—especially when the coaches aren't around?
Are we living out ubuntu? Or are those just words on the back of our shirts too?"

The group quickly realized where Cooper was going.

Kade was the first to raise his hand. "I think our ship is pretty strong right now, Cooper. The younger guys are really coming along. They are getting beat up a little bit at practice, but they are giving us a great look on the scout team. They definitely aren't afraid to make a mistake."

Trey jumped in: "Our sideline energy was awesome during the game. They're really into it! That makes a huge difference on the field."

"I love it," Cooper said, smiling. "We need to shine a light on that kind of behavior. Great leaders catch champions, not criminals. Too often, leaders shine an unintentional light on poor behavior by focusing on it all the time.

Coach Frost and I are constantly looking for ways we can continue to grow this culture, and right now we haven't been doing a great job of recognizing the behavior we want in our team. Recognition and celebration are vital—and often overlooked—aspects of servant leadership. So, here's what we're going to do."

Cooper pulled out a bag of coins. Looking closer, Easton could see they had the word "UBUNTU" on one side and their team values on the other.

"Starting this week, we'll begin our Weekly Shout-Outs. Each week, you all will pick two players from our team who are living out our values. Guys who are modeling ubuntu for the rest of us. As the leaders, you will stand in front of the team, present them with this coin, and tell them why you picked them."

Cooper set the bag of coins back down.

"As human beings, we want to be a valued member of a group. Getting one of these coins will be meaningful, yes—but the real value is the genuine, authentic recognition they'll get from their teammates. We want to reward the right behavior around here. This is a good start."

Cooper pushed the bag of coins across the table to Kade. They were sturdy, shiny, and gold.

"Lastly, I'm going to ask you to be intentional about not only picking guys who are living out our values but picking guys who are *rarely recognized* for their effort. Think about the guys who do the dirty work behind the scenes, who are serving and sacrificing for the good of this team, and who expect nothing in return. Everybody matters in this program, and we're going to show it," Cooper explained.

"You've got about fifteen minutes to make your decisions until the team meeting starts in the auditorium." With that, Cooper and Coach Frost left the room.

In the auditorium, Coach Frost started the meeting with two claps. The team replied with two claps, crisply delivered in unison.

"Tonight is the start of another new tradition: Weekly Shout-Outs. We're going to recognize some outstanding individuals in this program—not for their performance in the game on Friday, but for positively living out our values each and every day."

Coach Frost signaled the Leadership Council to come to the front. Kade took the stage and grabbed the microphone.

"Johnny Wilson, come on up here."

The undersized sophomore defensive back looked confused as he walked to the front of the auditorium. Kade handed him the coin and turned back to the team.

"We want to recognize Johnny because he works his butt off on the scout team every week. He gets knocked down on almost every play in practice. But every time, he gets back up with a positive attitude." Kade looked at Johnny, who stared sheepishly at his feet.

"He sacrifices so *we all* can succeed. When I think of ubuntu, I think of Johnny."

The team clapped, and Coach Frost saw a giant smile appear on Johnny's face. It warmed him up. Trey approached center stage next, calling forward senior offensive lineman Dawson Cook.

"I've known Dawson since we were six years old. He lives out our values every single day. At practice, at school, on the weekends—Dawson represents everything great about our culture. He truly inspires me to be a better person. Dawson is the epitome of a servant leader."

Trey turned to Dawson and handed him the coin.

"Dawson volunteered to be on the scout team as a *senior*. Coach Frost said he's never seen that in his life. But Dawson wanted to do it because he knew it was how he would help the team most effectively.

I mean, I saw this dude filling up water bottles at the JV game last week. For *sophomores*. Who else would do that?" Dawson grinned as he admired the ubuntu coin.

"I could go on and on—I mean, I love the kid. But I just wanna say, I'm thankful that Dawson is on our team." He gave Dawson a hug.

The Aviators felt more connected than ever. They didn't know it yet, but they were about to face adversity that would require every bit of that positive momentum.

CHAPTER 27

E + R = 0

"I'M SICK OF this. I'm sick of all of this! Everyone on this team! I'm sick of trying to carry you losers!"

Coach Frost could hear Easton screaming as he entered the locker room after the embarrassing loss. The Aviators had just been absolutely demolished by their rival school on their home turf. It was an implosion of epic proportions.

Everything that could go wrong went wrong for the Aviators. Turnovers, penalties, missed assignments—there were plenty of those. But to Cooper and Coach Frost, the most disappointing part of the night was the team's complete internal collapse. Players were taking plays off, arguing with the referees, and fighting with each other and the coaches on the sidelines.

"Easton, settle down," Coach Frost said firmly as he approached Easton in the middle of the locker room.

"*Settle down?*" Easton was yelling now. "I'm obviously the only one who actually cares about winning on this team. All of this leadership and culture crap is total bull—"

Coach Frost cut him off. "Out in the hallway. Now."

Easton paused for a second with a look of rage in his eyes. Finally, he threw open the door and stormed into the hallway with one of the assistants behind him.

The team was shaken. Silent. Coach Frost addressed them for a moment before stepping out into the hallway. He took a deep breath, gathering every bit of his patience before talking to Easton.

"Easton, I understand that tonight was tough, but your behavior is completely unacceptable." Coach Frost paused, his eyes piercing Easton.

"We need you to step away from the team for a few days. This is completely out of line."

"What are you talking about!" Easton barked back at him. "This team needs me!"

"If you can show that you're willing to embrace the values that *you* helped to define, and apologize to your teammates—we'll welcome you back with open arms.

Honestly, though, Easton, I'll be upfront with you. Trust isn't the only thing you're going to have to earn back. You also have to earn back your playing time. Ryan's getting the start next week."

Easton was stunned, but his shock lurched to anger. "Love, huh? You talk about love and then you do this to me. What a fake!"

"Easton, this *is* love. Love is the reason I'm holding you accountable right now." He turned back toward the door to the locker room.

"I hope someday you'll understand that."

The boys settled into the film room the following Sunday afternoon. Everyone was thinking about the elephant not in the room, but nobody wanted to say anything about it.

In years past, this would have been a moment when Coach Frost came down on the team hard. But this year, Cooper convinced Coach Frost to let him start things off.

"When things got tough on Friday, we cracked," Cooper shared. "And I want to be clear—it wasn't just Easton who fell short of our values. We underperformed as an entire team."

The room was silent. Cooper wrote an equation on the board.

$$E + R = O$$

"This equation is like gravity. It's a law. It doesn't matter if you like it or not." He tapped his marker on the board.

"The *E* stands for events. The *R* stands for response. And the *O* stands for outcome. In one game—even in just one practice—we face hundreds of events. The ways we respond to those events ultimately combine to create the outcome we get."[7]

Cooper paused to let the team digest it. "Help me out. What were some of the *events* we had to respond to on Friday?"

The players thought for a moment.

"The referee blowing a call." Trey surprised everybody by speaking up.

Cooper smiled. "That always seems to be a favorite start. Definitely an example of an event. What else?"

The answers started coming in. Dropped passes. Penalties. Sacks. Fumbles. Injuries. Coaches yelling at us. Fans. Weather. Teammates' attitude. The list was endless.

"Exactly!" Cooper exclaimed. "Everything starts with awareness. Before you can purposefully respond to these events, you must be ultra-aware that they exist. Is there any team in the league that doesn't have to respond to events like this at some point?"

---

7 E + R = O has been made famous by Tim Kight and Brian Kight.

The group shook their heads.

"Of course not. Everybody does. Great teams don't face fewer challenges than everyone else. They've simply trained themselves to respond *better* to those challenges. Owning their response becomes their superpower."

Cooper motioned to the screen he had set up. "I want to play some clips for you I cut up from the film."

Cooper pushed play. It was a montage of Aviator players reacting negatively to events: there was Sebastian getting into it with his own teammate after a miscommunication, players yelling at the refs, players looking like discouraged zombies on the sidelines.

Replaying the shortcomings was a challenging truth for the group to relive. But Cooper didn't let them stay in the past.

"The thing about your response is that it is contagious." After a pause, Cooper continued slowly. "And I want you to really understand this: your response becomes an event for your teammates.

Whining and complaining after a bad referee call. Sulking if you don't start. Giving up on plays. Below-the-line responses *accumulate*. They build off each other, and eventually they snowball into negative outcomes. We all felt the truth in this the other night."

Cooper looked around the room with a laser focus.

"The good news is the opposite is also true. Above-the-line responses can accumulate too. Choosing to focus on what you can control, encourage your teammates, and dig in deep when things get hard.

Owning our collective response in the toughest moments can become our greatest separator.

It's easy to respond well when things are going our way. But it is in the toughest moments when we need this training the most."

Cooper turned the group's attention back to the projector screen.

"I have one last play I want to show you. We were down seventeen points with a minute to go, and I saw one of our guys do this."

On the screen, the players watched the opposing running back break free up the right side into what looked like another easy touchdown. But from the left side of the screen, Trey entered like a bullet, sprinting down the ball carrier and tackling him on a diving play just before the end zone.

"This—*this* is the type of response we are after."

Cooper turned off the screen. "What would have happened if we responded to every event with the intensity, the hustle, and the grit that Trey did on that play?"

Kade jumped in. "We would've *dominated*."

The group nodded, starting to understand.

"All the hopes you have as an individual and a team depend on your willingness to consistently respond well to events.

Football creates an awesome training ground for you to become elite in responding. After that final whistle blows, you may be done playing, but you are just getting started responding to events.

Your future spouse won't care how many touchdowns you scored. But they will care how well you keep your cool in tough situations.

Your future boss isn't going to care if you were the team's leading tackler. But your boss will care if you can respond creatively under pressure.

If you have kids someday, they won't care if you were a starter on this team. But they will care how well you can respond to a tough day and still be a great dad.

At some point, your opportunities as a football player will run out.

But your ability to respond under stress won't.

As coaches, we want to win as much as you do. But even more important than that is this: We want to know that our players have become more resilient, gritty, and caring people that will make great husbands, great fathers, and great employees later in life."

Cooper paused and scanned the room slowly. They could tell he was serious.

"We're a month away from the playoffs. If we want our best when our best is needed, it's all about our collective response."

CHAPTER 28

ATTACK MURPHY

AFTER WRAPPING UP practice the following Thursday with a successful two-minute drill, Coach Frost pulled the team together.

"We learned last Sunday about the importance of our response. There are a lot of unfortunate events that can transpire throughout a game, throughout a year, and throughout a lifetime. However, if we focus solely on our response to those events, the outcome will be significantly better.

One way to improve the effectiveness of our response is to change the lens in which we view the event. If we can shift our perspective on our problems, we'll have a much better opportunity to respond effectively," Coach Frost explained.

"Now, has anyone heard of Murphy's Law?"

Trey raised his hand. "Yeah, my grandma used to talk about it all the time. It basically means anything that could go wrong will go wrong."

"That doesn't sound like a very positive way to view events, Coach," Sebastian interjected.

Coach Frost smiled in agreement.

"A lot of people get in a cycle of negative dialogue revolving around unfortunate circumstances in their life. They often ask themselves, 'Why do bad things always happen to me?' As if there is a black rain cloud that follows them around like in one of those old cartoons.

The truth is that unfortunate things happen to everyone. Some people simply respond better. Starting now, we are going to put our own spin on Murphy's Law. We are going to attack Murphy.

Instead of cycling into the internal dialogue and asking why bad things always happen to us, we are going to attack any unfortunate events together, as a team.

By giving our challenges a name, we are giving ourselves a common opponent. An opponent that we will conquer together," Coach Frost wrapped up.

The next night did not go as planned. The Aviators' offense struggled without Easton leading the way, but they still found themselves leading 10–6 late in the fourth quarter.

The defense was the only reason they were in the game, holding the Richland Raiders to two field goals. In fact, the lone Aviator touchdown came on an amazing pick-six by Trey in the second quarter. After that, the Aviators were only able to muster up a third-quarter field goal.

The inability to move the ball on offense frustrated Coach Frost. With less than three minutes left in the game, the Aviator offense was backed up on their own seven-yard line. They clung to their four-point lead and hoped to figure out a way to run out the clock.

Unfortunately, on the first play of the drive, the running back fumbled the football, giving it right back to the Raiders.

The turnover devastated the sideline. It meant the worn-down defense would have to take the field with their backs against their own end zone, needing yet another stop to win the game.

That's when Trey put his hands up in the air, signaling everyone to stop.

He looked his tired teammates in the eyes, and then he screamed at the top of his lungs, "Here is Murphy—let's attack him!"

The Aviator defense dug deep. They stopped two runs, broke up a pass, and foiled a QB scramble to the left. The offense got the ball back and ran the clock out. Victory.

After the game, Coach Frost gathered the team to address them.

"This is one of the prouder moments I have had as a coach. Not because we won the game, but because of how you responded.

When you are on a team, and some of your teammates are not pulling their weight, it's easy to point fingers, make excuses, and blame others. This can easily divide a team, and I've seen it happen many times.

Tonight, it would have been easy for the defense to get frustrated and turn their back on the offense, especially late in the game when the emotions were the highest.

But instead of turning your back on your teammates, you turned your focus to Murphy. You attacked Murphy, together—*as a team*," Coach Frost said, as chills ran down the back of his neck.

"Trey, that was one of the finest leadership moments I have seen in my coaching career. A lot of people can lead when things are going well, but true leadership is shown during times of adversity."

Trey looked up at him sheepishly. "Thanks, Coach."

"Unfortunately, a lot of leaders tend to hide when times get tough. You stepped up when we needed you the most," Coach Frost said with a proud smile.

"You all stepped up."

CHAPTER 29

FROM BREAKDOWN TO BREAKTHROUGH

It was just after midnight on Friday night, and Coach Frost was up grinding film after an Aviator win. That was when he heard it: two distinct knocks at his door that cut through the silence.

This can't be good, he thought.

"Coach?"

The muffled voice was familiar. Opening the door, he saw Easton, soaked with rain and looking desperate. Tears welled up in his eyes.

"Easton? What's going on? Come on inside." He stepped in, and Coach Frost grabbed him a towel to dry off.

"I didn't know what to do, I didn't know where to go," Easton stammered.

He continued, "It's my dad. He came home from the bar, and he came up to my room, and...and he just started getting in my face. He was drunk, and he just wouldn't stop. Telling me I'm worthless. That I screwed my life up."

Coach Frost put his arm around Easton. "C'mon over here and take a seat. Let's talk about it."

Easton took a deep breath and finally got an exhale he had been needing for the past hour. He shared more about what was going on. Coach Frost could feel his heart pounding in frustration as Easton shared what he was going through.

"I'm sorry you've had to go through this, Easton," Coach Frost shared. "None of what your dad said to you is true, Easton. I've been your coach for—what? Three years now? I've been so proud to see the man you're becoming. Making a mistake doesn't make you a failure. It's an opportunity to learn."

There was no playbook for how to support Easton in a moment like this. But just being next to him, *there for him*, felt right. Over the next twenty minutes, Coach Frost listened intently and helped Easton gain more clarity.

Easton wiped away a tear as he calmed down. He shared, "Coach, I abandoned you guys. How can I make up for that? I'm not a good teammate. I'm not a good leader. I'm just not what everyone expects me to be. I've been in my room for a couple days feeling like such a failure, trying to figure out how I can change. And I just don't know what to do."

Coach Frost hesitated, trying to figure out how to deliver the honest truth that Easton asked for in an emotionally charged moment.

"Easton, you bring so much to our team. You need to be *you*. But you must align with *us*." Coach Frost began choosing his words intentionally.

"You did fracture your trust with them, but trust can be rebuilt," Coach Frost continued. "To be honest, Easton, this isn't the first time your actions hurt your teammates. At times, your arrogance blinds you of where you can grow, and you quickly point fingers at others."

Easton looked surprised by Coach Frost's honest feedback.

"I guess I do come across as too confident in myself at times. I can see how that becomes arrogance," Easton replied.

"Not quite." Coach Frost disagreed with a caring smile. "Arrogance doesn't come from confidence. It exposes the absence of it.

Arrogance is the way you've learned to protect yourself from the Twin Thieves."

Easton locked in on Coach Frost's words. He had heard similar feedback from many coaches, but this was the first time he understood.

"And it's important to know that you aren't alone, Easton." Coach Frost continued. "I know how it feels to fall into the trap of arrogance and break the trust of those you lead. Every leader makes mistakes and experiences breakdowns.

The question now is: *can you turn this breakdown into a breakthrough?*"

"A breakthrough?" Easton questioned.

"Yes," Coach Frost responded, "I've learned that there are two guarantees in life—you will have opportunities and you will have adversity.[8] The challenge is: you often don't know when they are coming, and sometimes you can't tell the difference between the two.

This is an opportunity for you to build true humility."

Easton nodded his head slowly. Coach Frost could tell that mentioning the word "humility" made him uneasy.

"Humility is the opposite of arrogance." Coach Frost continued. "True humility helps you see your strengths and your areas to improve. It protects you from falling prey to the blind spots arrogance creates. Humility helps us rise above the Twin Thieves."

"I want to be clear." Coach Frost paused to make sure Easton followed. "I never want you to lose your swagger. I just want you to be so tough that you are willing to own your weaknesses. Because you can't beat something that you don't even see."

Easton listened intently and then responded. "So how do I begin practicing humility and showing my teammates I'm serious about being back out there?"

---

8 Brian Kight quote

"Well," Coach Frost said, "Tomorrow, you can start by showing up early to practice and giving a heartfelt apology to your teammates. You're Ryan's backup now, and you have to support him like he supported you.

Over the next week, you'll have some unique opportunities to get some momentum back."

"Okay," Easton said. "Okay, I will."

Coach Frost put his arm around Easton. "Ultimately, what you did last week will not determine your future, but how you respond to it will. In life, you will always have a story to tell.

Every story worth reading has some adversity in it. How you respond to that adversity is what can make that story great.

In order for you to have a testimony, you have to be tested."

When Easton left, Coach Frost felt a sadness wash over him. He knew what Mr. Hayes was like—but it'd never registered to him how it affected Easton's home life.

But the more he thought about it, the more he saw hope in the situation. Easton coming to him felt like another step in the right direction.

CHAPTER 30

GET TO VERSUS GOT TO

THE FOLLOWING MONDAY, Easton followed his coach's advice and delivered a genuine apology. After the brief team meeting, he and the rest of the team headed to the field and were surprised by the amount of equipment organized in six different stations around the field.

"Bring it in!" Coach Frost shouted to the team. Once all the players gathered around, he introduced the unique opportunity they had. "When Cooper came aboard, he shared that one of the most powerful events his teams did throughout the year was hosting a camp for kids with special needs. Today, he is helping to bring this opportunity to us."

Cooper said, "First, thank you for being here this morning. As you will see, this event is impossible without you. We've talked a lot about the Twin Thieves. Well, today will be a unique opportunity to face the fear of failure and the fear of judgment.

Today isn't an ordinary practice, but don't be fooled. You will still get a chance to better your best. In fact, this is one of the most important practices of the year."

Cooper motioned to the entrance and continued, "In a few minutes, kids of all shapes, sizes, and abilities will be showing up and counting on you to make their day great. You may feel a bit nervous and outside of your comfort zones. So let me simplify this.

As you look around, we have different stations set up to help you accomplish the one mission you are on today: serve your partner, and make it the best hour for them possible.

There isn't one script that will work. Just meet your participant at their level and figure out what they like and want to do. If you are fully engaged and bring awesome energy, everything will take care of itself."

There were more player mentors than participants, so Cooper asked the team to partner up. Sebastian and Easton went together and were excited to meet their partner, Noah. Noah was a first grader bursting with energy and a big smile. Braces lined his legs, making his walk a bit rigid.

After introducing themselves, Noah's mother shared, "Noah, tell Easton and Sebastian about your cleats."

Noah turned his feet, showing his cleats off like a prize. "I got these brand-new for camp today. They are my fast shoes!"

Noah did his version of hot feet just to show how fast they were. His mother joined back in with a wink. "In fact, Noah was so excited to get these cleats and play that he hasn't taken them off. He's been clicking around the house for the past two days. Yes, he even slept in them!"

She paused with a look of deep gratitude. "So thank you for making this happen today. But don't let those braces fool you. Noah is faster than you think."

Noah's excitement was contagious. Sebastian and Easton both had a huge grin on their face.

"*Let's go!*" Noah cut off the conversation and started making his way toward the tackling dummies. Sebastian and Easton ran, laughing, after him.

For the duration of the clinic, Sebastian and Easton gave everything they had to Noah. All their fear and hesitation seemed to evaporate as they helped him do things together that he couldn't do alone.

They chased him around as he scored touchdowns.
They fell on the ground as he stiff-armed them.
They created a touchdown dance to do anytime he scored.

They helped him catch, throw, punt, and kick.

When the final whistle blew, Easton and Sebastian hoisted Noah onto their shoulders like he was royalty. And in that moment, waving to his mother, who snapped hundreds of pictures between her tears of joy, Noah felt like he was the king of the world.

After saying goodbyes, Cooper brought the group back together to hear their reflection on the camp.

Sebastian shared first, "Our partner was Noah. It was amazing how excited he was to be here. Get this. He got brand-new cleats just for today. And he was so excited that he wore them for two days straight!"

The group smiled, feeling the warmth and energy coming from Sebastian.

Kade spoke up. "The biggest thing to me is how pumped they were to just come out here. I know I can forget how lucky we are to get to do this every single day."

Cooper smiled after Kade's response and shared: "You just articulated the power of perspective."

After a pause, Cooper went on. "The truth is changing one vowel can change your life. And that change is switching 'I got to' to 'I get to.' It is simply changing an *o* to an *e*—but the difference is massive.

This time of the year, the season can get long. You're tired. You've been around the same people for a long time. It can be easy to lose perspective and get caught in the 'I got to' trap:

I got to go to practice.
I got to go to my morning lift.
I got to watch film tonight.
I got to go on that long bus trip.
I got to cheer from the bench.

When you see life through the 'I got to' lens, everything becomes an obligation. It can start to feel like a job.

But elite teams avoid the lie of 'I got to' and keep a perspective of 'I get to.' They remember that every moment together is a gift. That some of the very things they get caught seeing as a burden would be seen as a blessing by somebody else."

Cooper turned to Sebastian and Easton. "Can you imagine how excited Noah would be to get to play under the lights on Friday nights? Or how much he would love to get to run freely and do sprints?

I challenge you all to be intentional with your language.

You don't 'got to' do anything. But you 'get to' do many things:

I get to practice and play a sport I love.
I get to lift so that I get stronger.
I get to watch film so that I can improve.
I get to go on that long bus ride with my teammates.
I get to be a part of a team.

Marcel Proust once said that 'the real voyage of discovery consists not in seeking new lands but in having new eyes.'

I hope today helps you to see things from a greater perspective of gratitude. Only you control your perspective. Thank you for sharing your time with us today."

CHAPTER 31

MUDITA

WITH JUST TWO weeks to go before the playoffs, Coach Frost gathered the players in the video room for their weekly meeting. The screen was pulled down, paused on a wide-view shot of their last game.

When everyone got settled, Coach Frost kicked things off.

"I want you to watch this fifteen-second clip and tell me what sticks out to you."

He hit play on the clip. Ryan dropped back, loaded up, and threw a beautiful pass down the left sideline. Sebastian extended, made the catch, and galloped into the end zone for an eighty-yard touchdown. It was the play of the game, and the players went nuts seeing it again.

"So what did you see?" Coach Frost asked once the excitement died down.

The responses came in from the group.

"What a pass by Ryan!"

"Offensive line did their job to give him time."

"Awesome route and grab by Sebastian."

"I agree with you all," Coach Frost said. "But I also saw something different that I want to highlight. Let's watch it again, and this time, keep your eyes on the sidelines."

As they watched it again, everybody understood what Coach was getting at. As Sebastian ran the eighty yards, you could see Easton, clipboard in hand, sprinting down the sidelines in pure joy and excitement. He was the first person to meet Ryan as he came back, giving him a monster hug and hyping him up.

Coach Frost paused the film.

"This is the stuff I love to see."

Easton smiled sheepishly in the third row. Coach Frost walked away from the computer and back toward the players.

"I want to introduce you all to a word: *mudita*. Mudita is a Sanskrit word that doesn't have an English equivalent. It means being authentically joyful for other people's success.

An unfortunate part of being on a team is that not everyone can be in the spotlight.

We'll always have more players on the sidelines than we do on the field. That's why it's impossible to build a great culture without an incredible sideline."

Coach Frost paused and glanced at Easton. He was locked in, hanging on every word of the coach's speech.

"Some of the most dangerous threats to a culture are jealousy, envy, and infighting. Very quickly, teams can go from breaking down an *opponent* to breaking themselves down *internally*.

Mudita is the opposite of that.

Mudita is me jumping up and down like a crazy man at my daughter's youth gymnastics meet when she nails her routine.

Mudita is when the sidelines go crazy after the defense makes a huge stop on fourth down.

Mudita is what you just saw on the film from Easton, leaving his personal ego behind to go all in on his teammates' success.

Mudita is rare in our society. Jealousy, envy, and bitterness are common.

But our culture is rare. We are uncommon. We are built *differently*.

To the The Twin Thieves, mudita is kryptonite—because when you see the success of others as *your own* success, you won't be limited by fear, insecurity, and self-doubt.

The Twin Thieves are obsessed with your stats, your plays, and your accolades.

But mudita is about *our* progress, *our* commitment to each other, and *our* success as a team.

In my opinion, the toughest people aren't the ones scoring the touchdowns and making the tackles. Often, the toughest people are the ones on the sidelines, dying to get in the game, but not letting the Twin Thieves dominate their mindset."

Coach Frost lifted up the screen, and the acronym "FAMILY" was written on the board. "A lot of teams say they are a 'family,' but very few teams behave like family. Families sacrifice for each other, families love each other.

FAMILY, as it is written here, means Forget About Me, I Love You. This is more than an acronym—it is a selfless mindset. It is about deeply caring for your teammates and being authentically happy for their success. It's about making mudita part of how we do things."

Coach Frost turned to his QB.

"Easton, a month ago, you wouldn't have done what you did on that play. I want you to know that your growth is inspiring. Keep preparing, keep showing mudita, and good things will happen to you. We are all proud of you."

The room erupted in applause. Coach Frost was smiling ear to ear. His team was back and better than ever. It was time for the playoffs.

CHAPTER 32

THE FARMER'S WATCH

It was official: the Aviators were headed back to the state playoffs.

Seeing the bracket, Coach Frost was conflicted. He felt more excited than ever to see how his team would handle the playoff atmosphere after a season of so much growth. But he also couldn't shake the thought of how many times the Aviators had been here before, only to crumble in their first game.

At practice on Tuesday, Cooper could sense Coach Frost's anxiety was spreading to the team. Everybody seemed tight. After Coach Frost reflected on the practice, Cooper shared a story that had helped his teams in the past handle the nerves of playoffs.

"There was once an old farmer who loved his grandson as much as anything. To demonstrate his love, he gifted his grandson a special watch. The watch had been passed down for many generations—and he decided it was time for his grandson to have it.

The grandson treasured the watch and knew how important it was to his family. He rarely ever took it off his wrist.

One day, the boy was playing with his friends in the haymow of the family farm. They jumped from bale to bale, tackled each other, played games till the sun went down. But at one point, the boy noticed something that made his heart drop to the floor.

His watch was gone.

He couldn't believe it. The chances of finding it in all that hay were nearly impossible. He was hopeless. The boy searched like a madman, throwing hay everywhere. With every minute he looked, his concern crept closer to full-blown *panic.*

Thoughts raced through his head:

How could I do this!
My grandpa is going to be so disappointed.
I'm such an embarrassment!

After finally giving up, exhausted and frustrated, the boy decided to tell his grandpa. It went much better than the boy thought. His grandpa even told him he'd help him find it. The boy was certain they'd looked everywhere. He told his grandpa there was no hope.

When they entered the haymow, the boy started pointing out all the places he'd looked. The barn looked like a tornado had gone through it. But before they got closer, his grandpa raised his hand and asked the boy to be silent.

The two of them stood in the middle of the haymow, motionless. Just when the boy was about to explode in confusion and frustration, he heard it.

Tick, tick, tick, tick, tick…

The grandpa smiled at his grandson and walked toward the noise. He rolled over a bale, dusted off the hay, and picked up the shiny watch. He handed it back to his grandson with a loving smile, and they walked out together."

Cooper paused and looked from one side of the group to the other.

"Pressure is a privilege. A lot of coaches and players would love to be experiencing this pressure right now. Don't run from the fear of losing. *Be grateful for the opportunity* to succeed.

We've prepared for every game like it is the state championship. We don't have to do anything differently than what we've already done to get our best.

While our opponent experiences chaos in critical moments, we trust our training to find clarity and calm. This is a competitive advantage.

We don't press under pressure.
We pause and then execute."

CHAPTER 33

THE TIGHTROPE WALKER

WITH EASTON EARNING his starting spot back at quarterback, the Aviators put their training to work and won their first playoff game. Finally breaking through and getting their first playoff victory propelled the group forward.

They carried that momentum into the state quarterfinals and rolled to another victory. Everything felt like it was coming together.

After so many years of first-round exits, Coach Frost believed this could really be the Aviators' year. He was locked in, but he could tell their semifinal matchup with the Dodgeland Jaguars was pulling at his players' focus. The Jaguars were the defending state champions and had most of their players returning.

On Thursday afternoon, Coach Frost discussed his feelings with Cooper and sent a message to the players.

Please meet Cooper in the field house before heading to the field.

As the players walked in, they saw Cooper at center court, holding a long piece of wood.

The players circled around Cooper, confused what the two-by-four had to do with practice. Cooper asked them all to take a knee as he laid the board on the basketball court.

"Who would like to earn a quick buck?" Cooper asked with a smile. He pulled a dollar bill out of his pocket.

"Who is willing to walk across this board for a dollar?"

Every single hand shot up in the air. Cooper selected Easton to walk across the long, skinny board. Easton easily put one foot in front of the other, heel to toe, all the way across without a problem.

Cooper handed Easton the dollar bill and smiled. "Nice work, Easton. Now, I have another dollar bill in my pocket. This morning I asked the custodian to place the same size two-by-four across those rafters," Cooper explained while pointing up to the high beams hovering over the gym floor.

"I'll give you another dollar to walk across the board up there, Easton."

Easton looked all the way up to the beams then looked at Cooper.

"No way!" The words jumped out of his mouth. "Not worth a dollar, man!"

"Why is that?" Cooper asked. "It's the same size board. What changed?"

"Yeah, well, what if I fall?" Easton asked sheepishly. He motioned to the one on the ground. "A little different than stepping off this one."

"Ding, ding, ding," Cooper said with a smirk.

"Let me tell you a true story.

The Flying Wallendas were a family of high-wire performers who were famous for their death-defying performances. In 1978, Karl Wallenda, the elder and leader of the Flying Wallendas, had one of his biggest performances coming up.

For the first time in his life, he talked to his family and friends about falling.

'What if I fall...what if I fall? There is no net to catch me—what if I fall?'

Now, understand this—Karl had been walking across a tightrope for over thirty years, and this was the *first* time he realized there wasn't a net," Cooper said with a smile. The players chuckled.

"Tragically, Karl ended up falling to his death. This exceptionally skilled man, who had completed thousands of high-wire walks in the past, fell victim to one of the Twin Thieves: the fear of failure.

When you spend your time worrying about failure, you, too, increase your chances of taking a fall. Where our focus goes, our energy flows."

Cooper paused and looked at Easton.

"Easton, when I asked you to walk across the board above the gymnasium, your focus immediately went to falling instead of focusing on simply walking across the board. When your focus is on failing, that's what you'll do.

Tell me—what other specific times do we focus too much on failure?" Cooper asked the group.

Sebastian raised his hand.

"Sometimes when I line up at receiver and I know the ball is coming my way, I will say to myself, 'Just don't drop the ball.' And a lot of times, I end up dropping it. I guess I should start focusing on catching it instead of *not* dropping it."

"Exactly!" Cooper exclaimed. "How about one more example?"

Trey spoke up.

"When I get a blitz call, all I can think about is *not* jumping offsides. Next thing you know, I'm either jumping offsides or I'm late on the blitz because I am so scared about screwing up."

"Excellent," Cooper said with a smile. "Guys, I understand that we have an important game tomorrow. A crucial one. But in reality, it's just another football game. A football game you have played many times—and played extremely well.

As tomorrow approaches, focus on simply walking across the board like you have done hundreds of times before. Put one foot in front of the other.

Focus on what you want to achieve, not what you want to avoid."

Cooper blew his whistle. "Alright, Coach Frost is waiting for you on the field. Let's go!"

Everyone got up and headed out the door to practice. Cooper spotted Easton walking through the mob of bodies back toward center court.

"Can I buy that board for a dollar?" Easton asked with a smile, handing Cooper his dollar back. "I'd like to keep it as a reminder."

CHAPTER 34

SURRENDER

THE AVIATORS CLICKED on all cylinders in the state semifinals and dismantled the defending state champions with a 33–13 victory.

Among all the hype, Cooper noticed that Kade was a bit quieter than usual.

After practice on Monday, Cooper approached him. "Kade, what's going on? It seems like you have a lot on your mind."

Kade looked up from his locker. "I've just been thinking about how much this would mean to our community if we could finally win a state championship. If I'm being honest though, the closer we get to winning it all, the more scared I am of losing it.

I don't know. I guess I just care too much."

"I definitely understand what you mean," Cooper said with a smile. "But I'm going to challenge you to care *even more* than what you do right now."

Cooper's response surprised Kade.

"I want you to care so much that you are willing to *surrender the outcome.*"

Cooper continued to explain. "Jack Nicklaus is arguably the greatest golfer of all time. He once said, 'The reason I win so much is because I'm okay losing.'"

"Okay losing?" Kade interjected, confused.

Cooper smiled. "Now, he didn't say he liked losing or preferred it. But he knew that even if he gave it his everything and lost, he was still going to be okay.

He surrendered the outcome and ended up winning more because of it.

A lot of people mistakenly think that if you succeed more, the Twin Thieves will finally disappear. Personally, I've found the opposite to be true. The closer you get to achieving dreams, the stronger the Twin Thieves get.

That is why surrendering the outcome and having a laser focus on the things inside your control is so powerful."

Cooper opened up his bag and pulled out a book. "Can I read you an excerpt from one of my favorite books, *Chop Wood Carry Water?*"

Kade nodded, and Cooper started reading.

> The ultimate illusion of the human experience is control. The person you want beside you in battle is the guy who has surrendered the outcome, and surrendered to the fact that he might die. When you surrender the outcome, you are freed up to be at your best, to be in the moment, and to trust your training. It is the one who has surrendered the outcome who ironically has the greatest chance of survival.
>
> It is the one who has surrendered the outcome who has the greatest chance of success. It is the one who has surrendered to the fact that he could fail, who has the greatest likelihood of not failing. Until you surrender the outcome, you will always be the greatest enemy to your own success. In order to reach your greatest potential you must *commit, surrender,* and *trust.*
>
> Surrendering the outcome doesn't mean you care less about the outcome or your process. It doesn't mean you don't give your very best. It simply means that you have surrendered the outcomes that are outside of your control. Many days, I surrender things that I desperately want to control, but know I don't have control over. Surrendering the

outcome is about having peace with that which is outside of our control without sacrificing the effort or care of what is inside of our control.[9]

Cooper closed the book and put his arm around Kade. As the two walked back to the locker room, no more words needed to be said. Kade knew what needed to be done.

---

9 Judah Smith quote from Joshua Medcalf's *Chop Wood Carry Water*

CHAPTER 35

THE STATE CHAMPIONSHIP

THE DAY OF the state championship had finally come. The Aviators were set to take on the Fillmore Bulldogs.

It was just four hours before the game that Coach Frost and many of the players had dreamt about for years. After the players finished their pregame meal, Cooper stood up in front of everyone.

"Are you up for one more story?" he asked the group with a smile.

The players exchanged glances. Cooper's stories had become famous inside the team.

"Back in 1977, there was a highly anticipated boxing match between the heavily favored Eugene 'Cyclone' Hart and an unknown challenger named Vito Antuofermo. Cyclone was well-known as a physically gifted puncher. Vito, on the other hand, didn't have any obvious physical gifts—but he had some serious intangibles.

From the opening bell, the bigger Cyclone dominated the fight. He was knocking the smaller Vito all over the ring. But by the fifth round, something funny happened. Cyclone started to tire out as Vito absorbed blow after blow. Cyclone was losing focus and becoming discouraged.

Vito seized the moment. He delivered a series of quick, decisive blows that knocked Cyclone down and ultimately ended the fight.

Afterward, they both returned to their makeshift locker room. Just a thin curtain separated the two. As Cyclone sat silently, he could hear Vito's cornermen discussing who would take him to the hospital.

Then he heard Vito speak up.

'Every time he hit me with that left hook to the body, I was sure I was going to quit. After the second round, I thought if he hit me there again, just one more time, I'd quit. I was on the brink of collapse. I thought the same thing after the third round and the fourth round. But he just never hit me there again.'

Cyclone started to weep. Really softly at first. Then harder. He was crying because, for the first time, he understood that Vito had felt the same way he had—and even worse.

The only thing that separated the guy celebrating and the guy crying was what they had *done. They both felt hurt. They both felt pain. They both felt exhausted.*

But Vito kept swinging while Cyclone gave in."

Cooper paused as he tried to make eye contact with each and every player.

"You never know when your competition is on the brink of collapse. *The key is* to *stay in the fight.* No matter what happens tonight, just keep swinging. Not for yourself, but for each other."

The first half of the state championship did not go as planned.

The Aviators gave up a quick score on the first drive. Easton threw an interception the next possession that was returned for a touchdown. Then they had a touchdown called back due to a pass interference call on Sebastian. It was a mess. Before they knew it, it was halftime, and they were down 28–7.

"Everybody gather round!" Coach Frost was standing on a bench in the locker room, making sure he could see every player on his team.

The players expected a drawn-out pep talk from the coach, explaining the things they needed to change. They got something entirely different.

"You guys are built for this moment," Coach Frost yelled out. "E + R = O. We all know the event. The question is: how are you going to respond?

I have a feeling you're going to have one hell of a response. Leaders, this is your ship." Saying nothing more, Coach Frost exited the locker room.

Easton took the initiative. He grabbed the two-by-four he'd bought from Cooper and stood on the bench. He was laser focused.

"All right, boys! Give me your eyes!

We have walked across this board before," Easton barked at his teammates. "We have been through much tougher fights than this.

We have battled the Twin Thieves. We have gone toe-to-toe with Murphy. Coach is right: we are built for this.

We know exactly who *we* are!
We won't press under pressure.
We function out of freedom, not fear.
We win with relentless execution of the fundamentals.
We don't need to do anything different. We just need to keep swinging.

Whatever happens in the second half, just know that I love you guys. And I'll keep swinging for you until the lights in the stadium go out. Who's coming with me?" Easton screamed as he hopped down and headed for the field.

The team joined him. The locker room erupted.

The second half started off with a methodical drive by the Aviators for a touchdown. Despite taking nine full minutes off the clock, there was no sign of panic. They'd walked across this board before. They were ready.

The defense forced a quick three-and-out to get the ball back to their offense.

On second down, Easton delivered a strike to Sebastian for a seventy-two-yard touchdown. The crowd went absolutely ballistic. Just like that, it was a seven-point game heading into the fourth quarter.

The Bulldog offense stalled, but so did the Aviators'. The final minutes started to tick away. Time was not on their side.

With less than two minutes left, the Bulldogs had shifted into clock-chewing mode. The defense needed to come up with a stop.

Trey inched closer to the line, laser focused on what he needed to do.

Blue eighteen! Blue eighteen! Set, hut!

He exploded out of his stance, found the hole, and devoured the halfback. The ball came loose! As the pile thinned out, the team could see little Johnny Wilson clutching the football.

"Offense, let's go!" Coach Frost yelled out. The crowd echoed his excitement.

Down by seven with 1:36 left, the Aviators needed to go sixty-seven yards with only one timeout. The pressure was heavy.

Easton stepped into the huddle.

"All right, guys. This is a Farmer's Watch moment. Everyone take a deep breath." Easton paused and slowly exhaled with the group.

"We've done this two-minute drill every Thursday for fourteen weeks. This is nothing new. Let's just walk across that board. One foot in front of the other."

Easton kicked off the drive by connecting with Sebastian on a smooth post route down the seam. Forty-three yards to go. After a twenty-yard run and a smooth screen play, they'd landed at the seven-yard line with four seconds left on the clock. Trailing seven points, the Aviators needed a touchdown.

Kade snapped the ball. Easton faked a handoff to the tailback and then snuck it to Sebastian on the jet sweep. Sebastian waltzed into the end zone, completely untouched. He'd never smiled this big in his life.

Coach Frost took his final timeout and brought everybody in. A feeling of déjà vu resonated through the group as they all felt how far this team had come from just over a year earlier.

"Okay. What do you all think? You want to kick the extra point or go for two and win this thing?"

Everyone knew the answer. The team would no longer allow the Twin Thieves to rob them of opportunities.

"Let's go for it, Coach!" Easton said.

Coach Frost smiled. "All right, you know the play. Trips left, tailback motion, Auburn. I believe in you guys," Coach Frost said, looking directly at the tight end who was going to be on the receiving end of Easton's jump pass. The huddle broke.

The fans watching couldn't believe their eyes. Even the announcer televising the game shared his surprise as the offense ran back onto the field.

"Why go for it? Why not kick the extra point?"

The Bulldog defense scrambled back into position. The line shifted as each defender found his matchup. Everybody seemed to be in a shock of surprise. The announcer set the stage.

"Oh, boy. Here we go, this is it! Coach Frost rolling the dice on the biggest stage."

Even with the external commotion, Coach Frost found an internal calm. Once he saw the tailback motion out of the backfield, he knew the tight end would be wide open in the back of the end zone.

"Hayes drops back...Plenty of time..."

Easton let go of the ball. It floated in the air for what seemed like an eternity.

"He lofts it to the tight end...wow! He catches it! It's over! It's over! Aviators win!"

The announcer's excitement matched the roar of the crowd.

Coach Frost couldn't believe it. It had all come to fruition. He stood next to Cooper, admiring the beautiful chaos in the back of the end zone.

The hugs and handshakes went around endlessly, and Coach Frost prepared to address the team at midfield. But at that moment, he was overcome by an emotion he didn't expect: sadness.

He'd always pictured this moment to be the happiest of his life. But now, holding the championship trophy—he realized that the journey with this group was complete. Tears rolled down his cheeks.

As he gathered the team to address them one more time, a single thought ran through his mind:

I'd give this hunk of metal back in a second if it meant I could spend one more week with this team.

CHAPTER 36

THE TEN-YEAR REUNION

As HE WALKED through the doors of Tanner's Sports Grill, Easton couldn't stop smiling. It'd been years since he'd sat in these red vinyl booths. The distinctive smell of burgers and fries instantly brought the memories he shared with his teammates back to life.

Easton's entrance was marked by hoots and hollers from across the restaurant. Coach Frost came and gave him a big hug.

"It's good to see you, Coach," Easton said. It was comforting to see his face after so many years.

"You too, Easton."

Behind Coach Frost, Easton saw Kade, towering above the rest of the team. He walked up and gave him a big bear hug. They caught up for a while, talked about their families, their careers, their lives after high school. When the conversation died down, Easton brought up the thing that'd been on his mind for years.

"You know, Kade, I was always jealous of you."

Kade smiled nervously. He thought Easton might be joking.

"C'mon man. You were All-State. You were the MVP. You were the starting QB! You were on TV, in the paper. You were the one that got all the girls," Kade said, punching Easton on the arm playfully.

Easton chuckled. "Yeah, yeah. But the team voted *you* captain. And that means something." He paused and surveyed the players who'd gathered.

"I'll never forget that day," he continued. "It felt like an absolute sucker punch. The one thing that I wanted most was to be our team captain, and there you were, picked instead of me. I could never understand it while we were playing.

But I remember on the last day of school, I asked Coach Frost: 'Why'd the team pick Kade instead of me?' And I'll never forget the answer.

Coach said, 'Easton, you are one of the best players I've ever coached. You were one of the best players in the *state*! Kade had nothing on your talent. But you know what made him outstanding? He wanted the *team* to be the best in the state.

Kade stayed late in the weight room to help his teammates. He'd drive kids home if they needed a ride. Whatever anybody needed, Kade was their guy. And he did all of this without asking for anything in return. The values we have? He *lived* them, each and every day.'

I'll always remember the last thing he said: 'Easton, you wanted to be the best player on the team. Kade wanted to be the best player *for* the team.'"

Kade shifted around uncomfortably. He looked down at his feet. This was a lot to take in, but he could feel Easton's sincerity.

"And you know what?" Easton asked. "He was 100 percent right. I'm so grateful I had you as a teammate, Kade. Tonight's gonna be great."

Before the two could continue, they were interrupted by a loud "*Cooooop!*"

Cooper made his rounds, giving a hug to every player in the room. "It's so wonderful to see you all!" he yelled out to the crowd. Easton could tell he was still spry and sharp as ever.

The night went on, and the team got lost reminiscing. Laughter echoed around the restaurant as players ran through story after story from the good ol' days.

As things started to die down, Coach Frost stood in front and called for everyone's attention.

"I want you to know how much I appreciate you all being here. Every team is special to me—but this group is unique. *You* were the agents of change in our program. *You* took our program to the next level. *You* changed our whole culture for the better.

I saw each and every one of you grow in so many ways—and you saw me grow along with you."

Coach Frost embraced the moment with pride as he looked at the men he'd helped to mold.

"We shared some incredible memories. I've heard people talking about the bus rides, going away to camp, eating meals together, Turf Toughness Days, the Difference Maker camp, and all the times you sat in these very booths. But you know the one thing I haven't heard? The fact that we won a trophy. That we *won our first state championship.*

There was a point in my career when I would've given anything to win that trophy. I thought it would mean everything to me. But you guys helped prove that wrong. It's not the trophy I treasure the most—it's the bonds we built on the journey together.

It's about the butterfly effect.

Everyone leaves a legacy, but the world's most transformational people create a butterfly effect. A wave of positivity that affects lives far away from their own, long into the future."

Everybody in the room locked in on Coach Frost like it was ten years earlier.

"I'm excited to see the butterfly effect that the incredible leaders in this room create," Coach Frost continued. "Leadership isn't reserved for the football field. Our world is in desperate need of people committed to transformational leadership.

Your spouses. Your kids. Your colleagues. Your employees.

They all need you to be the best leader you can be."

The alumni in the room nodded their heads, understanding the truth in Coach Frost's words.

"Never forget the principles that you've learned during our time together.

Remember that great leadership doesn't happen by accident. It is the result of many hours pouring into the hearts and minds of the people you serve.

Remember that connected teams are powerful teams.

Remember that there is nothing soft about love.

A team bonded by love builds a toughness that fear never could.

Remember that your greatest opportunities will require you to confront the Twin Thieves. Don't run from the fear of failure and the fear of judgment. Go toward them."

Coach Frost paused and soaked in the moment.

"I want you all to know I still love you the same way I did ten years ago.

My love will always be unconditional and unchanging.

Your football days may be over, but I know you all will continue tackling the Twin Thieves in your own ways. Please know this: when days get dark, or when you feel stuck, or when things just aren't working out—remember that you'll always have me in your corner.

I'm proud of you.

I love you all."

11 WAYS GREAT LEADERS BUILD GREAT TEAMS

1. **Serve** - The best leaders are servant leaders. Focus on serving the people you have the privilege to lead.

2. **Lead Yourself** - Before you can lead others, you must lead yourself first. The best leaders model the way by doing the dirty work, having a growth mindset, and consistently living out the standards.

3. **Empower People** - Leadership is a river, not a reservoir. Empower the people you have the privilege to lead by giving them ownership.

4. **Be the Buffalo** - Your greatest opportunities will require you to confront the Twin Thieves. Don't run from the fear of failure and the fear of judgment. Go toward them.

5. **Deliver the Mail to the Right Address** - Provide direct feedback to the people that need to hear it the most. Put challenging issues on top of the table and have courageous conversations.

6. **Catch Champions** - Shine a light on the behaviors you want to see by making celebration and recognition an essential part of your team's culture.

7. **Water the Bamboo** - Success is not microwavable. Great leadership is not an accident. Great leadership occurs when we pour time into the hearts and minds of the people we serve.

8. **Become an Elite Listener** - Great leaders are great listeners. Your team won't care how much you know until they know how much you care, and the fastest way to show someone you care is to truly listen.

9. **Embrace Change** - Change is inevitable, but growth is optional. Great leaders and elite cultures are constantly learning, evolving, changing, and growing.

10. **Focus on Your Response** - There are a lot of events that are outside of our control. Elite leaders embrace these events and focus on how they respond.

11. **Love Your Team** - The greatest counterpunch to fear is love. Connected teams are powerful teams. Bonds of love endure in a way bonds of fear never could.

THANK YOU FOR READING!

THANK YOU FOR taking the time to read our work. We hope you enjoyed the lessons and would love to hear which ones meant the most to you through our contacts below. Being self-published, we rely on the support of people like you. We are so grateful to anybody who goes out of their way to share our work.

WITH LOVE,

Steve Jones
Twitter: @CoachJonesKHS
Instagram: @CoachJonesKHS
Email: Stevejonesspeaking@
gmail.com

Lucas Jadin
Twitter: @Lucas_Jadin
Instagram: @Lucas_Jadin
Email: Lucas@traintobeclutch.
com

WANT TO EQUIP YOUR LEADERS AND BUILD A STRONGER TEAM?

WE PROVIDE THE services below both virtually and face-to-face to accommodate organizations of all sizes. Please know that our services are authentic and vulnerable. We push you to take ownership of your growth, and sometimes growth requires you to get uncomfortable.

Services

Keynotes:
Thirty-minute to ninety-minute experiences designed to inspire and challenge your team.

Workshops:
One-hour to nine-hour experiences where we customize our principles to meet your team where they are at. These sessions are a two-way experience with dialogue and engaging exercises.

The Clutch Leadership Process:
We partner with businesses, athletic programs, and school districts to create a series of workshops that build off each other to take your leaders to the next level.

Mentorship Process:
A one-on-one coaching experience customized to meet you where you are and help you grow. This option is for people serious to go to the next level and ready to invest in themselves.

The Twin Thieves Training Guide:
We put together an awesome training guide to walk through the Twin Thieves. You can email us for more information.

To get more information on any of these, reach out to us:
Lucas: Lucas@traintobeclutch.com or visit T2BC.com
Steve: Stevejonesspeaking@gmail.com

MORE BOOKS BY LUCAS JADIN

Win in the Dark

Many people crave the attention that comes with mastering a craft—chasing the limelight, the spotlight, and the glamour. But behind every "overnight success" is tens of thousands of hours training and failing in the dark.

Win in the Dark is a powerful story about a boy named Niko chasing a big dream. Guided by his Grandpa Marco, he comes to understand that it's not the physical aspects of the journey that challenge and change him the most—it's the mental demons and barriers he must battle in the dark.

The dark is the unseen hours of gut-wrenching, tedious work.
The dark is where you confront fear, hesitation, and self-doubt.
The dark is where you give your everything without knowing if your everything will be enough.

And when you emerge after years of training in the dark, *they* often undercut your work by having the audacity to call you an "overnight success" and "freakishly talented."

They don't realize that talent is only the starting line, that it's overrated, and that it's never enough.

There are treasures, both tangible and intangible, for those with the courage to keep returning to battle in the dark and embark on the road less traveled to explore the edges of human potential.

It's here where you transform into the best version of yourself and pay the price of admission for a chance at capturing dreams that once seemed like fairy tales.

Welcome to the dark.

Thank you to the people below for giving us feedback on the book and helping us make it the best that it can be.

Tony Holler

Eric Hulting

Dean Mastche

Tim Bergstrom

Tina Beauvais

Dan Eslick

Dan Casey

Joe Holschuh

Jarrett Dawson

John Zimmerman

Michael Graber

Thank you to these members of the Launch Group that went above and beyond to help share this story.

Nate Werner

Amy Knoche

B. J. Buss

John Woods

Shelly Hotzler

Simon Thomas

Mike Elkin

Jared Cecil

Matt McFadden

Steve Considine

Caroline McCombs

Konner Beste

Nate Crandall

Ben Halder

Reid Behrendt

Trisha Kroll

Simon Leslie

John Adams

Brad Fortney

Jon and Kylie from Trifluence Coaching

THANK YOUS FROM STEVE

THANK YOU TO everyone who supported me, challenged me, and encouraged me throughout my life. It is impossible to list everyone, and I am sure I missed a lot of names, but please know that I am very grateful.

Carrie, thank you for all of your support and unconditional love. Being a coach's wife can be very difficult at times. You have sacrificed in so many ways to allow me to coach and lead a football program. You are an awesome mom and an amazing wife. I love you and I am so grateful for you!

Cooper, you are such an amazing gift! Your energy, your sense of humor, and your genuine care and empathy for others is inspiring. I love you so much!

Lucas, thank you for going on this journey with me. The process of writing this book along with our relationship over the years has helped me grow so much. Most importantly, thank you for being such a great friend. You are an incredibly consistent and authentic person in my life. Katie, thank you for support and for your friendship. Trey, Kade, and Cole—you three are rock stars!

Our coaching staff: Thank you for the countless hours and all of the hard work you have poured into our players, our community, and our football program. As I have said for many years, I am blessed to work with the best coaching staff in the state. I appreciate your support of this book and your friendship.

Thank you to all of our past and present players. I have learned so much from each of you. You are the reason I coach. As we know, the rings and trophies collect dust, but the memories will never fade. I am thankful for the relationships with each of you. I am honored to be your coach. I love you guys!

Mom and Bob, you are both missed a great deal. You are in our prayers each night.

Thank you to John, Kim, David, and Jaden for your unwavering support and advice throughout my entire life.

Mike, Shannon, Kellan, and Elise thank you for showing what true resilience looks like as a family. You are an inspiration in so many ways.

Suzy, thank you for all of your encouragement throughout my life.

The Hermsen Family, thank you for being my second family. Your unconditional love and support for each other and for me is amazing. I love you!

Thank you to Tim Bergstrom for being a great friend and a mentor in my life. You and your family are a wonderful example of *how great leaders build great teams.* You bring many of the principles from this book to life in your amazing organization at Bergstrom Automotive.

Coach Miech, thank you for your support over the years and always believing in me.

Thank you to Jarrett, Greg, and Eric for the memories, the laughs, and your long-lasting friendship over the years.

Thank you to Jack Stoskopf for creating a "Starfish Moment" for me during such a pivotal time in my life. You inspired me at a young age to make a positive difference in others.

The Kimberly School District, thank you for being so progressive in offering leadership courses for all of our students over the past twelve years and for allowing me to discover my passion for teaching leadership.

Kimberly High School Leadership Students, thank you for electing to push yourselves outside of your comfort zone by practicing authentic vulnerability and for stepping into the "arena" of leadership at a young age. I have learned a lot from each of you.

Thank you to Bailey Marash for your creativity in designing our book cover. It is a privilege to work with a former student and football player from our program.

Thank you to Pat, Ed, and Jeannie Von Feldt for being my extended family as I grew up. Your generosity, consistency, and care is something I am eternally grateful for.

Thank you to all of the businesses, schools, teams, hospitals, and companies who took a shot at bringing in a high school football coach to speak with your team.

Thank you to Bob Chapman, Brian Wellinghoff, and all the wonderful people at Barry-Wehmiller for your mentorship, friendship, and guidance in my leadership journey. I admire how you continue to show the world that you can truly care for people and still be incredibly competitive and successful at the same time.

Joshua Medcalf, thank you for your support of Lucas and me in writing this story. Also, thank you for inspiring me to have the courage to write a book and hit publish.

THANK YOUS FROM LUCAS

THERE ARE SO many people who have influenced me on this journey. The list below just begins to scratch the surface. Thank you to all of you who have supported, encouraged, and helped me along the way.

Katie, thank you for all the love that you share with me and our kiddos. I appreciate all the unseen hours that you put in to make our family the best team it can be. I couldn't ask for a better partner in life!

Trey, Kade, and Cole, you bring me so much joy and don't even realize it. I love you!

Steve, thank you for being an inspiration, supporter, and an incredible friend. You have shown the world what winning with love looks like. I'm excited to continue this journey. Carrie, thank you for your continued support and helping make this book great. Cooper, thank you for your consistent flow of energy!

Mom and Dad, thank you for modeling what unconditional love means every single day. Logan, Levi, and Jenny...thank you for all your support. I love you all.

Joshua, what can I say? I couldn't ask for a better business partner and friend. You've supported me, challenged me, and pushed me in so many different ways. Thank you for showing me what it is like to put first things first.

Thank you to my grandparents, in-laws, aunts, uncles, cousins, and friends I consider family... You've been in my corner since day one and helped inspire the stories in this book.

Gene and Claire, thank you for creating a sanctuary where I seem to get my best ideas.

Thank you, Amber, for all of your work behind the scenes with T2BC. Joshua and I really appreciate it!

Joe, Darren, and Buss Family...thanks for getting me to go to that clinic where all this started.

Athletes and coaches from Appleton North High School, thank you for being my guinea pigs and biggest supporters. I learn from you daily what transformational leadership looks like.

Thank you, Appleton Area School District educators and administrators, for believing in me and supporting my work.

Thank you, Matt Hechel and Heidi Maase, for getting up early with me and helping bring mental skills to students.

Thank you to Erik Hanson, Matt Mineau, and my Appleton eSchool Mindset Mastery students for making mental skills a priority! I learn so much from you. Our world needs you to be courageous.

Thank you to my teachers and coaches from Freedom Schools. Your inspiration lives in me to this day.

Thank you, Jenni, Greg, and Dan from Fox West Academy. You showed me what great leadership looks like in the classroom from the beginning.

Erik and Tanya...thank you for your friendship and redoing my office. It was a game-changer in getting this done.

Thank you to all the people that have welcomed me into their teams, businesses, and schools. I hope you all know how much I appreciate you.

Thank you to the LA Dodgers. Gabe Ribas, George Lombard, Dave Roberts, Tony Capucilli, Raul Ibanez, and Jeff Kingston, thank you for our time together and allowing me to see inside an elite culture.

To my one-on-one mentorship clients, doing life with you is an honor.

To all of our Inspire Sports families, thank you for being a huge part of my life and inspiring me.

Made in the USA
Coppell, TX
15 April 2022

76596332R10096